RUDOLF STEINER (1861–1925) called his spiritual philosophy 'anthroposophy', meaning 'wisdom of the human being'. As a highly developed seer, he based his work on direct knowledge and perception of spiritual dimensions. He initiated a modern and universal 'science of spirit', accessible to anyone willing to exercise clear and unprejudiced thinking.

From his spiritual investigations Steiner provided suggestions for the renewal of many activities, including education (both general and special), agriculture, medicine, economics, architecture, science, philosophy, religion and the arts. Today there are thousands of schools, clinics, farms and other organizations involved in practical work based on his principles. His many published works feature his research into the spiritual nature of the human being, the evolution of the world and humanity, and methods of personal development. Steiner wrote some 30 books and delivered over 6000 lectures across Europe. In 1924 he founded the General Anthroposophical Society, which today has branches throughout the world.

NUTRITION

Food, Health and Spiritual Development

RUDOLF STEINER

Compiled and edited by Christian von Arnim

RUDOLF STEINER PRESS

Rudolf Steiner Press
Hillside House, The Square
Forest Row, RH18 5ES

www.rudolfsteinerpress.com

Published by Rudolf Steiner Press 2008

Earlier English publications: see Sources section on pp. 181–83

Originally published in German in various volumes of the GA (*Rudolf Steiner Gesamtausgabe* or Collected Works) by Rudolf Steiner Verlag, Dornach. For further information see Sources, pp. 181–83. This authorized translation is published by permission of the Rudolf Steiner Nachlassverwaltung, Dornach

All material has been translated or checked against the original German by Christian von Arnim

Translation and selection © Rudolf Steiner Press 2008

A catalogue record for this book is available from the British Library

ISBN: 978 1 85584 210 6

Cover by Andrew Morgan Design featuring a blackboard sketch by Rudolf Steiner from 18 July 1923
Typeset by DP Photosetting, Neath, West Glamorgan
Printed and bound by Cromwell Press Limited, Trowbridge, Wiltshire

Contents

Introduction

Nutrition is a subject which has firmly entered our general awareness today. From the growth of obesity in wealthy western societies to the quality of our food and the way it is produced, what and how we eat has become a subject of debate at all levels from government policy-makers to the home. Healthy eating has become just as much part of the debate around ecological lifestyles, sustainable agriculture, intensive farming and animal rearing, the value of organic foods and how we treat the planet as the overarching questions associated with global warming and the future of human development.

Rudolf Steiner may not yet in his day have had to grapple with wider ecological issues such as whether it is more ecologically sound to fly beans thousands of miles from Africa to European markets than to grow them closer to home in the colder European climate using hot houses which may leave just as large a carbon footprint because of the energy needed to heat them, but nutrition as a subject was well established. The investigation of the composition of foods and the effect on health of proper amounts of substances like carbohydrates, minerals, fats and proteins had started in its modern form in the mid-eighteenth century.

In 1770, Antoine Lavoisier, the 'Father of Nutrition and Chemistry', discovered the actual process by which food is metabolized. In the early 1800s the discovery was made that foods are composed primarily of four elements—carbon, nitrogen, hydrogen and oxygen—and methods were developed for determining the amounts of these elements. In the mid-nineteenth century the German chemist Justus Liebig undertook influential work on plant and animal physiology. It is worth noting that chemistry, along with the natural sciences and mathematics, was one of the subjects studied by Steiner during his student days in Vienna.

Yet while scientific and medical research into nutrition and healthy or harmful diets has, of course, moved on again in the 90 odd years since Steiner was lecturing on the subject, what is also clear is that one thing has not altered: the extent to which nutritional advice still keeps changing and sometimes contradicting itself as new research throws a different light on previously accepted axioms with regard to what is healthy or not so healthy for us to eat. That this was already an issue in Steiner's day is illustrated in his example of the daily portions of protein which it is advisable to eat.

Just like the delicate balance of our external natural environment, where an action in one part may have unexpected, not to say unintended, consequences in another, the human being also represents a cohesive and integrated 'sphere', both as a physical and a spiritual being. In this sense any dietary recommendation may produce unexpected results, which may not always be immediately apparent. And this is where Steiner goes far beyond current nutritional research (which is largely restricted to the effect of substances at a material level) in that he investigates the effect of foods on the whole human being at a much more fundamental level, including the spiritual elements permeating the physical body. In this way he avoids the potentially unexpected consequences of a one-sided materialistic perspective.

This approach gives his results a significance that has not lost any of its relevance, and is much more subtle. It recognizes that protein, for example, may have different effects depending on its source and that not only is the physical health of the human being influenced by the kind of food we eat, but also our spiritual well-being. In this wider view, eating the right kinds of food can either promote or hinder our development as whole human beings.

In terms of its structure, the book moves from the more general view to the particular. In the early chapters, Steiner describes nutrition and substances in the wider context of the human being as a spiritual entity and, indeed, against a cosmic background. On this basis, the later chapters then describe the actions and effects of particular types of food in greater detail. These lectures were given to different types of audience; some were made up of the general public while others were mainly anthroposophists following a path of spiritual development, so the tone also varies from the more general to the more intimate.

One thing which emerges clearly in all that Rudolf Steiner says about nutrition is that he never wishes to be prescriptive. At no point does he try and tell his audience what they should or should not be eating, whether or not they should follow a vegetarian diet, whether they should or should not smoke or drink alcohol. He repeatedly states that it is not his task to tell people what to eat or how to behave. The job of the scientist is to explain how things act and their effect—what people then do with that knowledge is entirely up to them. One reason for this may lie in the fact that the effects of a particular diet can be influenced by the particular circumstances of the individual. It may be better for a person to eat a meat diet, for example, at a certain stage of his life, and blanket prescriptions are simply beside the point because they leave the individual out of consideration.

But more fundamentally Steiner here, as elsewhere, never wishes to impinge on the freedom of the individual. Each person must recognize what is the appropriate diet for him at any given time. Although, as Steiner also points out, people in our modern age have increasingly lost the instinct for what is good or bad for them to eat, that is no reason for him to be prescriptive. It is up to each of us individually to work out what is the right course of action in our particular situation. Our diet not only determines our physical well-being, but can also promote or hinder our inner spiritual development. What Steiner wishes to do is give us the tools that can help us to understand how we can best promote our physical health and spiritual progress.

Christian von Arnim

1. Nutrition in the Light of Spiritual Science

Rudolf Steiner here looks at nutritional processes in broad outline in the context of the human physical and spiritual organization. He discusses the different ways that vegetarian and meat diets affect the inner human being and the relationship between human beings and animals and plants.

In the past I have spoken here on a variety of subjects concerning spiritual life. It may be permissible today, therefore, for me to touch upon a more prosaic theme from the standpoint of spiritual science. Problems of nutrition undoubtedly offer a more mundane subject than many we have heard here. It will be seen, however, that particularly in our age spiritual science has something to say even with regard to questions that directly affect everyday life...

It was a German philosopher, Ludwig Andreas Feuerbach, to whom the phrase 'A man is what he eats' is attributed. Many thinkers of consequence have agreed with Feuerbach that what the human being produces is basically the result of foods ingested by him, and his actions are influenced by the food absorbed in a purely materialistic way through his digestion. With so much discussion of eating going on, somebody might get it into his head to believe that the human being is indeed physically nothing more than what he eats. Now, we shall have several things to say on this point.

We must understand each other precisely as to the purpose of today's lecture and the intention behind it. We are not agitating in favour of particular tendencies, nor are we trying to be reformative. The spiritual scientist is obliged to state the truth of things. His attitude must never be agitatorial, and he must be confident that when a person has perceived the truth of what he says he will then proceed to do the right thing. What I have to say, therefore, does not recommend one course as opposed to another, and he who assumes that it does will misunderstand it completely. Merely the facts will be stated, and you will have understood me correctly if you realize that I am not speaking for or against anything.

Bearing this in mind, we can raise the question from the standpoint of spiritual science as to whether the statement 'A man is what he eats' does have a certain justification after all. We must continually bear in mind that the human body is the tool of the spirit. In discussing the various functions the body has to perform, we see that the human being utilizes it as a physical instrument. An instrument is useless if it is not adjusted correctly so that it functions in an orderly manner, however, and similarly our bodies are of no use to our higher organism if they do not function properly. Our freedom can be handicapped and intentions impeded.

When we as spiritual scientists consider our organism, we can ask ourselves whether we make our bodies unfit for the execution of the intentions, aspirations and impulses of our lives if we become bound by and dependent upon our bodies through an unsuitable diet. Is it not possible to mould the body in such fashion that it turns into a progressively more suitable instrument for the impulses of our spiritual life? Will we lose our freedom and become dependent upon our bodies if we ignore what is the right nourishment for us? What must we eat so that we are not merely the product of what we eat?

By asking such questions, we come to look at the problem

of nutrition from another perspective. You all know, and I only need allude to this generally familiar fact, that speaking purely materialistically, people continuously use up the substances that their organisms store and they therefore must take care to replenish them with further nourishment. Human beings must concern themselves with replenishment. What, then, could be more obvious than to examine those substances that are necessary for the human organism, that is, to find out what substances build up the animalistic organism, and then simply see to it that the organism is given them. This approach, however, remains an extremely materialistic one. We must rather ask ourselves what the essential task of human food is and in what way it is actually utilized in the organism.

I must stress that what I say about the human being is applicable only to him, since spiritual science does not consider the human being to be so closely connected with the animals as does natural science. Otherwise, one could simply state that the human organism is composed of proteins, fats, carbohydrates and mineral substances, and consequently search for the best method to satisfy human nutritional needs from them. But spiritual science holds to the principle that every material occurrence, everything that takes place in the physical sense world, is only the external aspect of spiritual processes. Indeed, even the nutritional processes cannot be purely physical, but as material processes they are really the external aspects and expressions of spiritual processes. Similarly, the human being is a unity even though the composition of his physical body appears to be a conglomeration of chemical events...

We need to be aware of the four elements which comprise the human being. To the researcher investigating spiritual matters, a person is not just his physical entity which can be seen and felt but the physical body is only one part of the human being. The physical body consists of the same chemical substances which can be found in nature. But the human being also has higher components of his being. Even the first one of these is supersensory in nature, has a higher reality than the physical body. It underlies the physical body and throughout a person's life fights against its decay. From the time that a person passes through the portal of death, the physical body is left to its own laws and decays. Throughout life, the life or etheric body fights against such decay. It gives the substances and forces a different direction, a different setting than they otherwise would have if they were left to themselves. This body is just as visible to clairvoyant consciousness as the physical body is to the eyes. Human beings have their life or etheric body in common with plants.

We know from other lectures that human beings additionally have a third element, the astral body. How is that composed? It is the bearer of pleasure and pain, cravings, drives and passions, everything we call our inner soul life. All those things reside in the astral body. It is spiritually visible, like the physical body is to physical consciousness. Human beings have this astral body in common with the animals.

The fourth component is the bearer of the I, of self-awareness. It makes human beings the pinnacle of creation, setting them apart from the things of earth which surround them. Thus we have the human being before us with three invisible and one visible element. They are in constant interaction. All of them together affect each single one and each single one affects all the others. That is why the physical body as we have it before us—I repeat that these things only apply to human beings—is an expression in all its parts also of the invisible components of human nature. This physical body could not contain in itself those elements which serve nutrition, reproduction, life as such, if it did not have the etheric body. All those organs which serve nutrition and reproduction, the glands and so on, are an outward expression of the etheric body. They are what the etheric body builds in the physical body. The nervous system in the physical body is, among other things, an expression of the astral body. Here the astral body is the actor, the creator. We might use the image of a clock or a machine built by a clockmaker or an engineer: the nerves are built similarly by the astral body. And the characteristics of the human blood circulation, the activity of the blood, are the outer physical expression of the bearer of the I, the bearer of self-awareness. In this sense the human physical body itself in a certain way also consists of four elements. It is an expression of the physical components of itself and its three higher elements. Purely physically, we have the sense organs; the glands are an expression of the etheric body; the nervous system of the astral body; and the blood of the I . . .

Now, you all know that human beings eat food derived from the vegetable, animal and mineral kingdoms, and with it they sustain their bodies. Let me emphasize again for the sake of those who are more narrowly inclined towards the care of the inner life that I am not speaking to mystics nor to anthroposophists who are striving to develop themselves spiritually in particular, but to everyone. Human beings take their sustenance from the animal, vegetable and mineral kingdoms. We must realize that plants represent the direct antithesis of human beings, and the animals represent the mean between the two. The external physical expression of this contrast is to be found in the breathing process. It is a familiar fact that human beings inhale oxygen, assimilate it and subsequently combine it with carbon which is finally exhaled as carbon dioxide, while in plants, which absorb carbon to sustain themselves, the reverse is true. In a sense, plants also breathe but their breathing process has a completely different significance for them. Hence, we can say that in a spiritual respect plants and human beings stand opposite each other.

We can become even more aware of this relationship by bearing in mind the influence of light on plants. The effect of deprivation of light on plant life is well known. The same light that maintains life in plants makes it possible for us to perceive the light-filled world of our surroundings. Light is also the element that maintains life in plants. This is physical light but it is also something more. Just as there is a spiritual counterpart to everything physical, so there is spiritual light in the physical light that rays down on us. Each time a human being rejoices over the brilliance of physical light he can say to himself, 'Just as when I see another person and it dawns on me that in this human being there lives a spiritual counterpart, so also I can imagine that in light there lives a spiritual counterpart.' Indeed, the spiritual light that permeates the physical sunlight is of the same kind and being as the invisible light that dwells within the human astral body. A portion of the spiritual light that permeates the cosmic realm lives within the astral body. It is, however, physically invisible and in this it can be seen that it is the opposite or complement of physical light.

The invisible light lives within us and fulfils a definite task. We might say that since they are opposites it is to physical light what negative magnetism is to positive magnetism. We perceive it in its external expression when we realize the relationships existing between physical body, etheric body and astral body, which in turn is permeated by the ego. It has often been explained that throughout life the etheric body fights against the deterioration of the physical body. Human beings as well as animals also possess an astral body and hence the inner light. Now, the function of this inner light is the opposite of that of external light. When external light shines on a plant, the plant builds up its living organism by producing proteins, carbohydrates, etc. Conversely, the task of inner light is to break things down, and this process of disintegration is part of the activity of the astral body. There is indeed a continuous dissolution and destruction of the proteins and other substances that we consume so that these substances are utilized in a sense to direct counter-effects against what external light has built up. Without this activity of inner dissolution a person could not be an ego being, and it is only by virtue of his ego nature that he can have inner experiences. So, while the etheric body is concerned with the preservation of the physical body, the astral body takes care that the food human beings consume is constantly built up and again destroyed.

Without this process of disintegration within the physical body, the astral body, in which the ego is incorporated, could not live a full life within the material world. As we have seen, there is an alternating process taking place between human beings and plants, that is, exhalation of carbon dioxide in human beings and absorption of carbon dioxide by plants; exhalation of oxygen by plants and inhalation of oxygen by human beings. These processes reach such extremes only between human beings and plants...

Let us consider how the ego can gradually take a central position within the bodily functions. Let us examine what the astral body does when it dissolves the substances assimilated by human beings. With regard to nourishment, an entirely different viewpoint must be stressed. The body, permeated by the ego, performs an action in disintegrating substances, and through this action something is created inwardly. The inner activity of consciousness particularly comes about through the astral body's processes of dissolution. Actions, activities are called forth by the process of destruction. First, inner warmth is produced and second, something that is less noticeable than inner body heat, the physical expression of inner light. Just as the internal warmth that permeates the blood is the result of the breakdown of proteins, so the activity of the nervous system is the expression of this inner light. With regard to its inner activity, the nervous system is also a result of a disintegration process—not the nerves themselves but the activity of the nerves, the actions within the nerves, that which makes possible imagination and calls forth thinking. It is this activity that can be called the physical expression of the invisible light and that is brought about through the degeneration and breakdown of substances.

Basically, as has been said, inner body heat is generated by the breakdown of protein. Inner light is produced within the organism as a result of protein. Inner light is produced within the organism as a result of processes involving fats, carbohydrates, starches and glucose, which are also utilized in the production of warmth and inner movement. All this represents the expression of the activity originating from the astral body. Human beings do not nourish themselves properly simply by ingesting the correct quantity of food, but rather when these inner processes can be carried out in the right way. The inner life is founded on them. Human beings are beings continually occupied inwardly with movement and animation and their inner life consists of these. If this inner life is not produced in the right way, it cannot react properly and a person then becomes ill.

The right kind of inner flexibility offers the foundation for the right solution of the nutritional problem. This statement points to the fact that all internal processes that human beings must execute must be carried on in the opposite direction from the processes of plants. A person must begin his processes where the plant processes leave off. A specific example will clarify what this means. When a person eats vegetarian food, it demands a great deal of his organism. Plant food does not contain much fat. The human organism, which is able to produce fats, is thus required to produce fat from something that in itself contains no fat. In other words, when a person eats vegetarian food, he must generate an activity within himself and make an inner effort to bring about the production of fats. He is spared this task when he eats ready-made animal fats. The materialists would probably say that it is advantageous for a person to store up as much fat as possible without having to make too much of an effort. Yet, speaking from the spiritual viewpoint, the unfolding of this inner activity signifies the unfolding of the actual inner life. When a person is forced to generate the forces that make it possible for him to produce fat on his own, then, through his inner flexibility, the ego and the astral body become master of the physical and etheric bodies. When a person eats fat, the result is that he is spared the task of producing fat himself. Yet, if he takes the opportunity to unfold his own inner activity through producing his own fat, he is made free and thus becomes lord over his body. Otherwise, as a spiritual being he remains a mere spectator. Everything that takes place in him in such a way that he remains a passive spectator becomes a heavy weight in him and hinders his drive to let the astral body come to full life. Thus, the astral body's inner flexibility comes up against an internal obstacle if it is denied the opportunity to produce its own fat.

The essential question now to be asked is what internal activities are aroused by what substances. Here we shall try to throw light on the relationships of vegetable and meat substances in human diets, and thereby to gain some idea of the manner in which animal and vegetable foods react in the human organism.

For a person to eat animal protein is not the same as for him to eat plant protein. Up to a certain point the inner processes of the animal are quite similar to those of the human organism, since the animal also possesses an astral body. Even though the animal astral body causes the breakdown of the synthesized substances of its physical body the human organism carries the processes a bit beyond the limits reached by that of the animals.

In reflecting upon the animals around us and by looking spiritually into their ways and characteristics, we shall, by comparing human beings with the many different animals, find distributed among the animals the various and manifold characteristics of human beings. In spite of the fact that one can point to great differences between various peoples, we must nevertheless conclude that it is each individual person who represents a species. Human beings appear to be the spiritual consolidation of all that can be observed distributed in the various animals forms. If one were to picture all the individual characteristics of the various animal species as being mutually complementary, one would arrive at the essence of what is contained in appropriate moderation in each individual person. Each individual animal one-sidedly contains within itself something of the forces that are harmonized within human beings, and its whole organism is constructed accordingly. Everything down to the most minute structure of substances is so organized in the animal kingdom that it is like a tableau of human characteristics spread out before one.

If a person is to find the physical expression of the characteristics of his astral body, he must strive to utilize all its forces. He must become master of his own inner processes and activate his astral body in such way that the plant processes are continued inwardly. In the food we consume from the animal kingdom, we not only take into ourselves the physical meat and fat of the animal but also the product of its astral body contained in these substances. When, through a vegetarian diet, we draw on the pure forces of our astral body, we call forth our whole inner activity. In a meat diet part of this inner activity is forestalled.

We can now proceed to consider the relationships of these two types of diet from a purely spiritual perspective.

If a person wants to gain increasing mastery over the inner processes of his body, it is important that he become correspondingly active in the external world. It is important for him to unfold certain external qualities such as stamina, courage and even aggressiveness. To be able to do so, however, it is possible that a person may not yet find himself strong enough to entrust everything to his astral body and may have to fall back upon the support of a meat diet.

It can be said that human beings owe everything that liberates them internally to the substances derived from plants. Faculties, however, that enable them to be actively engaged in earthly life need not necessarily grow out of the pure nature of their astral body. These qualities can also be derived from a meat diet. This fact that human beings are to become progressively freer while at the same time needing qualities that they can acquire with the help of impulses found spread out in the animal kingdom has induced them to resort to nourishment in animal food. If the eating habits of the people of those militant nations that have striven to develop qualities enabling them to unfold their physical forces are investigated, it will generally be found that they eat meat. Naturally, there are exceptions. On the other hand, a preference for an exclusively vegetarian diet will be found to prevail among people who have developed an introverted and contemplative existence. These two aspects of the problem should be kept in mind. A person, of course, can adopt either diet as a panacea if he wishes to propagandize rather than to act out of knowledge. Nevertheless, it is not without reason that a mixed diet has become acceptable to many people. To some extent it had to happen. We must admit, however, that even though a vegetarian diet might indeed be the correct one for some people purely for reasons of health, the health of others might be ruined by it.

I am speaking here of human nature in general, of course, but human beings must be considered as individuals if they are to find the right path to satisfy their needs with a vegetable or meat diet. Today, an extreme diet of meat naturally brings its corresponding results. If by eating meat a person is relieved of too large a portion of his inner activities, then activities will develop inwardly that would otherwise be expressed externally. His soul will become more externally oriented, more susceptible to, and bound up with, the external world. When a person takes his nourishment from the realm of plants, however, he becomes more independent and more inclined to develop inwardly. He will become master over his whole being. The more he is inclined to vegetarianism, the more he accepts a vegetarian diet, the more he will be able also to let his inner forces predominate. Thus, the more apt he will be to develop a sense for wider horizons and he will no longer restrict himself to a narrow life. The person who is fundamentally a meat-eater, however, limits himself to more narrow vistas and directs himself more rigidly towards one-sidedness.

Naturally, it is the task of human beings today to concern themselves with both aspects so as not to become impractical. A person can also be so completely unprejudiced as to have no judgement at all. Still, it is a fact that everything that limits human beings and leads them to specialization is derived from a diet of meat. A person owes to a vegetarian diet the impulses that lift him above the narrow circles of existence. An extreme diet of meat is definitely connected with a person's increasing dogmatism and his inability to see beyond the confines into which he was born. By contrast, if human beings would show more interest in the food coming from the realm of plants they would discover that they are able more easily to lift themselves out of their narrow circles. The person who abandons the task of fat formation by eating meat will notice that the activity thus forestalled erects a sort of wall around his astral body. Even if one is not clairvoyant but judges these matters only with common sense, one can tell from the look in a person's eyes whether or not he produces his own fat. It can be seen in the eyes of a person whether or not his astral body is obliged to call forth the forces necessary to produce his own fat.

Now it can be seen how two opposing conditions of character are created when a person takes his nourishment from either the plants or animals. We find that we indeed penetrate into the world through our organism and must again rise above it by means of the right kind of food. A time will come when a vegetarian diet will be valued much more highly than is the case today. Then thinking will be so flexible that human beings will be willing to investigate such matters knowing that what they believe today to be foolishness could, viewed from another standpoint, also have its merits. They will realize then that their whole physical and spiritual horizon can be widened through a vegetarian diet, thus counteracting the rigour of specialization within them. Particularly in certain areas of science, perspectives would be widened if vegetarian diets were to become prevalent.

Let me mention a few more examples to demonstrate that human beings are indeed what they eat and drink.

Consider, for example, alcohol, which is obtained from plants. It would take too long to explain the spiritual-scientific reason showing that alcohol produces physically and in an external way from the plant just what a person should develop physically within himself through his ego being centred within him. It is a fact inwardly perceived through spiritual science that when a person drinks alcohol, it takes over the specific activity that otherwise belongs wholly to the person's ego. A person who drinks much alcohol needs less food and his body will require less nourishment than is normally required in the process of combustion.

It calls forth forces that otherwise would be called forth by the ego's inner penetration. Thus, a person can externalize the activity of his ego by infusing his body with alcohol. Consequently, alcohol imitates and copies the activity of the ego, and you can understand why it is that people turn to it. To the extent, however, that a person replaces his inner self with such a substitute, to that extent does he become its slave. If otherwise qualified, a person will be better able to unfold the best forces of his ego when he abstains from alcohol altogether. By drinking alcohol an inner obstacle is created behind which something takes place that actually should and would be accomplished through the activity of the ego itself if the obstacle had not been produced.

Some foods have a specific effect of their own on the organism. Coffee is an example. The effect of coffee becomes manifest through its influence on the astral body. Through caffeine and the after-effects of coffee, our nervous system automatically performs functions that we otherwise would have to produce through inner strength. It should not be claimed, however, that it is beneficial under all circumstances for a person always to act independently out of his astral body. Human beings are entities who are not dependent on themselves alone. On the contrary, they are placed within the whole of life.

Coffee is also a product of the plant kingdom that externally has raised the specific plant process up a stage. Consequently, coffee can take over a certain task in the human being. Trained insight perceives that everything in the activity of our nerves that has to do with logical consistency and drawing conclusions is strengthened by coffee. Thus, we can let coffee take over in making logical connections and in sticking to one thought, but this, of course, is in exchange for a weakening of our specific inner forces. What I mean can be seen in the tendency of gossips at a coffee break to cling to a subject until it is completely exhausted. This is not only a joke. It also demonstrates the effects of coffee.

Tea works in a totally different and opposite way. When large quantities are drunk, thoughts become scattered and light. It might be said that the chief effect of tea is to let witty and brilliant thoughts, thoughts that have a certain individual lightness, flash forth. So we can say coffee helps those, such as literary people, who need to connect thoughts in skilled and refined ways. This is the positive aspect of the matter. The negative aspect can be observed in coffee table gossip. Tea, which tears thoughts asunder, is the opposite. This is why tea is, not without justification, a popular drink of diplomats.

It might be of interest to cite as a last example a food that plays an important part in life, that is, milk. Milk is completely different from meat in that it expresses in the weakest possible form the animalistic process brought forth by the astral body of the animal. Milk is only partly an animal product and the animal or human astral forces do not participate in its production. For this reason milk is one of the most perfect foods. It is suitable for people who want to abstain completely from meat but who do not yet possess sufficient strength to work entirely out of the inner forces of the astral body. Even from a purely external standpoint it can be seen that milk contains everything a person requires for his organism. Although this applies only in a restricted sense, it has little to do with the individual characteristics of a person.

Weak as well as strong organisms can gain support from milk. If a person were to live exclusively on milk for a time, then not only would his regular forces be awakened but it would also go beyond this. He would receive from it an influx of forces giving him additional strength. A surplus of forces would be acquired that could be developed into healing forces. In order to possess a force, it must first be acquired, and in milk we see one means of developing certain forces in ourselves. Those who are moved by the earnestness of life to develop certain psychic healing forces can train themselves to attain them. Naturally, we must remember that what is suitable for one is not suitable for all. This is a matter for the individual. One person is able to do it, another not. A person can if he wishes build up his organism in a wise manner. He can contribute towards the development of free, independent inner forces. So through spiritual science we come back to Feuerbach's saying mentioned at the beginning, 'Man is what he eats!'

The human being can nourish himself in such fashion that he undermines his invisible independence. In so doing he makes himself an expression of what he eats. Yet he ought to nourish himself in such a manner that he becomes less the slave of his nutritional habits. Here spiritual science can direct him.

The wrong food can easily transform us into what we eat, but by permeating ourselves with knowledge of the spiritual life we can strive to become free and independent. Then the food we eat will not hinder us from achieving the full potential of what we, as human beings, ought to be.

2. The Penetration of Substance with Spirit

This lecture looks at some fundamental aspects of nutrition in the wide reciprocal sweep of earthly and cosmic influences acting through the food we eat. But in a change of perspective it not only discusses how eating a vegetable diet affects the spiritual nature of human beings and animals, but also how the plant metamorphoses when it is eaten.

You will have gathered from what has been said so far that the human being's relationship to his environment is very different from what modern minds often conceive. It is so easy to think that what exists in the human being's surroundings, what belongs to the mineral, plant and animal kingdoms and is then taken into the body, that these external material processes which are investigated by the physicist, the chemist and so on, simply continue on in the same way in the human being himself. There can, however, be no question of this, for one must be clear that inside the human skin and its processes everything is different from outside it, that the world inside differs entirely from the world outside. As long as one is not aware of this, one will continually assume that what is examined in a retort or investigated in some other way is continued on inside the human organism; and the human organism itself will simply be regarded as a more complex system of retorts.

You need only recall what I said in yesterday's lecture, that everything mineral within the human being must be transformed until it reaches the condition of warmth ether. This means that everything of a mineral nature which enters into the human organism must be so far metamorphosed, so far changed that, at least for a certain period of time, it becomes pure warmth, becomes one with the warmth which the human being develops as his own individual temperature independent of the temperature of his environment. No matter whether it is salt or some other mineral that we absorb, in one way or another it must assume the form of warmth ether, and it must do this before it is used to build the living organism.

It is utter nonsense to imagine that some mineral from the outside world would simply transfer itself into the human body and make up some part of the skeletal system, the teeth, etc. Before anything can be part of the human form it must have gone through the completely volatile warmth-ether stage and then have been transformed again into a part of the living form of the human organism.

But something quite different is also connected with this. Solid substance loses its solid form when it is changed in the mouth into fluid and is then further transformed into the condition of warmth ether. It also gradually loses weight as it passes over into the fluid form and becomes more and more estranged from the earthly. But only when it has ascended to the warmth-etheric form is it fully prepared to absorb into itself the spiritual which comes from above, which comes from cosmic widths.

Thus, if you would gain an idea of how a mineral substance is utilized in the human being, you must say the following [a diagram was drawn]. There is the mineral substance; this mineral substance enters into the human being. Within the human being, passing through the fluid state, and so on, it is transformed into warmth ether. Now it is warmth ether. This warmth ether has a strong disposition to absorb into itself what radiates inwards, streams inwards, as forces from cosmic spaces, from the widths of the cosmos. Thus it takes into itself the forces of the universe. And these forces of the universe now become the spiritual forces which here imbue warmth-etherized earthly matter with spirit. And only then, with the help of this warmth-etherized earthly substance, does there enter into the body what the body needs to take shape and form.

So you see if, in the old sense, we designate heat or warmth as fire we can say: What the human being absorbs in the way of mineral substance is taken up to the level where it becomes of the nature of fire in him. And what is of the nature of fire has the disposition to take up into itself the influences of the higher hierarchies; and then this fire streams back again into all the human being's internal regions, and resolidifies to provide the material basis for the individual organs. Nothing that human beings take into themselves remains as it is; nothing remains earthly. Everything, and specifically everything that comes from the mineral kingdom, is so far transformed that it can take into itself the spiritual and cosmic; it then resolidifies into the earthly condition with the help of this.

Take a fragment of calcium phosphate from a bone, for instance. This is in no way the calcium phosphate which you find outside in nature, or which, let us say, you produce in the laboratory. It is the calcium phosphate which, while it arose from what was absorbed from outside, could only take part in creating the human physical form with the help of the forces that penetrated it during the time when it was changed into the warmth-ether condition.

This, you see, is why the human being needs substances of the most diverse kind during the course of his life in order to be able, in accordance with the way he is organized at each particular age, to transform what is lifeless into the condition of warmth ether. A child is as yet quite unable to change what is lifeless into the warmth-etheric condition; he has not enough strength in his organism. He must drink the milk which is still so nearly akin to the human organism in order to bring it into the condition of warmth ether and apply its forces to carrying out the truly extensive shaping and moulding that is necessary during the years of childhood to produce the human form. One only gains insight into the nature of the human being when one knows that everything which is taken in from outside must be worked on and thoroughly transformed. Thus, if you take some external substance and wish to test its value for human life you simply cannot do this by means of ordinary chemistry. You must know how much force the human organism has to exert in order to bring an external mineral substance to the fleeting condition of warmth ether. If it is unable to do this, the external mineral substance is deposited and becomes heavy earth matter before it has passed over into warmth; it remains foreign inorganic matter and is deposited in the tissues.

This may happen, for example, when the human being is not able to bring a substance that—though organic in origin—appears mineralized in him, namely, sugar, to the tenuous condition of warmth ether. It is then deposited in the organism without ever having reached the condition that it must achieve if the whole organism is to have part in everything it contains, and the very serious condition of diabetes develops. In the case of every substance one must therefore consider to what degree the human organism can transmute lifeless substance into warmth substance, whether the nature of that substance is already lifeless, as when we eat common salt, or whether it becomes so, as with sugar. In warmth substance, the organism, which is rooted in the earth, finds its connection with the spiritual cosmos.

Every deposit in the human being which remains untransmuted—as in diabetes—signifies that the human being does not find the connection with the spiritual of the cosmos for the substances present within him. This is only a special application of the general axiom that whatever approaches the human being from outside must be entirely worked over and transformed within him. And if we wish to look after a person's health it is of paramount importance to see to it that nothing enters into him that will remain as it was, nothing that cannot be dealt with by the human organism and transformed even if it is only quite minor in degree. This is not only the case with regard to substances; it is also the case, for instance, with regard to forces.

External warmth—the warmth we feel when we touch things, the external warmth in the air—this, when taken up by the human organism, must be so transformed that the inner warmth is at a different level from the warmth outside. External warmth must be somewhat transformed in us, so that this external warmth, in which we are not present, is laid hold of by the human organism, right down to the least particle of warmth.

Now imagine that I go somewhere cold, and because the cold is too intense, or because moving air or a draught creates fluctuations in temperature, I am not in a position to change the world warmth into my own individual warmth quickly enough. This means that I run the danger of being warmed by the world's warmth from outside like a piece of wood or a stone. This should not be. I should not be exposed to the danger of external warmth flowing into me as though I were merely some object. At every moment, I must be able to lay hold of the warmth from the boundary of my skin inwards and make it my own. If I am not in a position to do this I catch a cold.

That is the inner process of catching a cold. To catch a cold is poisoning by external temperature, of which the organism has not taken possession.

You see, everything in the external world is poison for the human being, actual poison, and it only becomes of service to him when, through his individual forces, he lays hold of it and makes it his own. For only from the human being himself do forces ascend to the higher hierarchies in a human way; whereas outside the human being they remain with the elemental nature beings, with the elemental spirits. In the case of the human being this wonderful transformation must happen so that the elemental spirits in the human organization may give over their work to the higher hierarchies. For the mineral in the human being this can only occur when it is absolutely and entirely transformed into warmth ether.

Let us look at the plant world. Truly this plant world has something of manifold enchantment to us when we begin to contemplate the plant cover of the earth with the eye of the spirit. We go out into a meadow or a wood. We dig up, let us say, a plant with its root. If we bring spiritual perception to bear upon what we have dug up, we find a wonderfully magical complex. The root shows itself as something of which we can say that it has become entirely earthly. Yes, a plant root—the coarser the more so—is really something terribly earthly. A root—especially a turnip root, for instance—always reminds one of a particularly well-fed alderman. Oh, yes, it is so; the root of a plant is extremely smug and self-satisfied. It has absorbed the salts of the earth and feels a deep sense of gratification at having soaked up the earth. In the whole sphere of earthly existence there is no more absolute expression of satisfaction than such a turnip root; it is representative of root nature.

On the other hand let us look at the flower. When we observe a flower with the eye of the spirit we cannot help but experience it to be like our own soul when it cherishes the tenderest desires. Only look at a spring flower; it is a breath of longing, the embodiment of a wish. And something wonderful streams forth over the world of flowers that surrounds us, if only our soul perception is delicate enough to be open to it.

In spring we see the violet, maybe the daffodil, the lily of the valley, or some plants with yellow flowers, and we are seized by the feeling that these spring-flowering plants would say to us: 'O human being, how pure and innocent can be the desires which you direct towards the spiritual!' Spiritual desire, desire bathed, as it were, in godliness, breathes from every spring flower.

And when the later flowers appear—let us go straight to the other extreme, let us take the autumn crocus—can one behold the autumn crocus with soul perception without having a slight feeling of shame? Does it not warn us that our desires can become impure, that our desires can be imbued with every kind of corruption? It is as though the autumn crocuses spoke to us from all sides, as if they would continually whisper to us: 'Consider the world of your desires, O human being; how easily you can become a sinner!'

Looked at thus, the plant world is the mirror of human conscience in external nature. Nothing more poetical can be imagined than the thought of this voice of conscience, which in us comes forth as though from a single point, distributed over the many different kinds of flowers that speak to the soul during the seasons of the year in the most manifold ways. The plant world reveals itself as the outspread mirror of conscience if we know how to look at it properly.

If we bear this in mind it becomes of special significance for us to look at the flowers and picture how the flower is really our longing for the light-filled spaces of the universe, how it literally grows upwards in order to send the desires of the earth streaming towards the light-filled spaces of the universe, and how on the other hand the substantial root fetters the plant to the earth; how it is the root which continually wrests those celestial desires away from the plant, wishing to change them into earthly ease and satisfaction.

And we learn to understand why this is so when, in the evolutionary history of the earth, we meet the fact that what is present in the root of a plant has invariably been laid down in the time when the moon was still one with the earth.

In the time when the moon was still one with the earth, the forces anchored in the moon were so powerful in the body of the earth that they hardly allowed the plant to become anything but root. When the moon was still with the earth, and the earth still had a quite different substance, the root element spread itself out and worked downwards with great power. We can picture the downward thrust of the plant's root nature spreading out powerfully, while up above the plant merely peeped out into the cosmos. We could say that the plants sent their shoots out into the cosmos like delicate little hairs. Thus we can sense that while the moon was still with the earth this moon element, the moon's forces contained in the earth's body itself, fettered the plant's nature to the earthly. And what was then transmitted to the being of the plant remains as a predisposition in the nature of the root.

After the moon had left the earth, however, a longing for the light-filled spaces of the universe unfolded in what had previously existed only as tiny little shoots peeping out into the universe; and now the floral element developed. So the departure of the moon was a kind of liberation, a real liberation for the plants.

But here we must also bear in mind that everything earthly has its origin in the spiritual. During the Old Saturn period— you need only take the description which I gave in my *Occult Science*—the earth was entirely spiritual; it existed only in the element of heat or warmth ether, it was all spirit. It is out of the spiritual that the earthly was formed.

And now let us contemplate the plant. In its form it bears the living memory of evolution. In its root nature it bears the process of becoming earthly, of assuming the physical and material. If we look at the root of a plant we also discern that it says something to us, namely, that its existence only became possible because the earthly and material evolved out of the spiritual. Scarcely, however, was the earth relieved of its moon element than the plant again strove back to light-filled spaces.

When we consume the plant as nourishment we give it the opportunity of carrying further, in the right way, what it began outside in nature, striving back not only to light-filled spaces, but to the spirit-filled spaces of the cosmos. This is why, as I said yesterday, we must take the plant substance within us to the point where it becomes aeriform, or gaseous, so that the plant may follow its longing for the wide spaces of light and spirit.

I go out into a meadow. I see how the flowers strive

towards the light. The human being consumes the plant, but within him he has a world entirely different from the one outside. Within him he can bring to fulfilment the longing which, outside, the plant expresses in its flowers. Spread abroad in nature we see the desire world of the plants. We eat the plants. We drive this longing towards the spiritual world within us. We must therefore raise the plants into the sphere of the air so that in this lighter realm they may be enabled to strive towards the spiritual.

The plant undergoes a strange and peculiar process in us. When we eat plant food the following occurs. If we have the root here below [a diagram was drawn], and above what strives through the leaf to the flower, then in this transformation into the airy condition we have to experience inwardly a total reversal of plant nature. The root, which is fettered to the earth for the very reason that it lives in the earth, strives upwards; it strives upwards towards the spiritual with such power that it leaves the striving of the flower behind it. It is actually as if you were to picture the plant unfolding below like this, and the lower can then be pushed up through the centre, so that the upper becomes the lower and the lower the upper [demonstration with a handkerchief]. The plant reverses itself completely. The part that has already achieved the level of the flower has had enjoyment of the light in its material striving, has brought the material up into the sphere of the light. For this, it must now suffer the punishment of remaining below. The root has been the slave of the earthly; but, as you can see from Goethe's theory of the metamorphosis of plants, it bears the plant's whole nature within it. It now strives upwards.

Inveterate sinners generally want to remain as they are. But the root of a plant, which as long as it is bound to the earth gives the impression of a well-fed alderman, is transformed and strives upwards immediately when it has been eaten by the human being; whereas that which has taken physical matter into the sphere of light, the flower, must remain down below. Hence in what belongs to the root element of the plant we have something which, when it is eaten, strives upwards towards the human head and really does this out of its inherent nature, while what lies in the direction of the flower remains in the lower regions; within the total metabolism it does not go up as far as the head process.

Thus we have the remarkable, the wonderful drama that when the human being consumes some kind of plant or vegetable—he need not eat the whole plant, because in each single part the whole plant is inherent (I refer you again to Goethe's theory of metamorphosis)—it transforms itself within him into air which, like an inverted plant, grows and flowers from above downwards.

In times when such things were known through ancient, instinctive clairvoyance, people looked at the external constitution of plants in order to see whether they were such as could be beneficial to the human head, whether the root already gave a strong indication of a longing for the spiritual. For when digestion is completed, what we have eaten of such a plant will seek out the head and penetrate it, so that it may there strive upwards towards the spiritual cosmos and enter into the necessary connection with it.

In the case of plants that are strongly imbued with astrality, for example peas and beans, even the fruit will remain in the lower human organism and be unwilling to rise up to the head, thus producing a heavy sleep and dulling the brain on waking. The Pythagoreans wished to be clear thinkers and not involve digestion in the functions of the head. This is why they forbade the eating of beans.

You see, therefore, that from what happens in nature we can divine something of nature's relation to the human being, and to what happens in the human being. If one pursues spiritual initiation science, one simply cannot imagine how materialistic science gets to grips with human digestion—matters are of course different with regard to a cow's digestion (about this, too, we shall have something further to say later)—by stating that plants are simply ingested. They are not simply ingested but completely spiritualized. The plant form in itself is inverted, so that the lower turns into the upper and the upper into the lower. No greater transformation can be imagined. And the human being immediately becomes ill if he eats even the smallest quantity of a plant where the lowest is not changed into the uppermost, and the uppermost into the lowest.

From this you will realize that the human being bears nothing in himself which is not worked on by the spirit; all substances taken into the organism must first be given a form which will enable the spirit to influence them.

Turning now to the animal world, we must be clear that in the first place the animal does have a digestive system and that plant substance is ingested. Let us take the herbivorous animals. The animal world takes the plant world into itself. This again is a very complicated process, for when the animal ingests the plant it does not have the human form to set against the plant. Within the animal, the plant cannot turn the above into the below and the below into the above, for the animal has its vertebral column parallel with the surface of the earth. This means that in the case of the animal what should happen in digestion is thrown into complete disorder.

What is below strives upwards, and what is above strives downwards. But the whole process gets dammed up in itself, so that animal digestion is something essentially different from human digestion. In animal digestion, what lives in the plant dams itself up. And the result of this is that, in the animal, plant nature is given the promise: 'You may indulge your longing for the widths of the cosmos'—but the promise is not kept. The plant is repulsed back to earth again.

Through the fact, however, that the plant is cast back to earth in the animal organism, there immediately penetrate into the plant not cosmic spirits with their forces—as with the human being in whom the reversal takes place—but certain elemental spirits. These are elemental spirits of fear and anxiety, the bearers of fear and anxiety. Spiritual perception can follow this remarkable process. The animal itself enjoys its nourishment, enjoys it with inner satisfaction; and while the food stream goes in one direction, a stream of fear from elemental spirits of fear goes in the other. Through the animal's digestive tract there continually flows along the alimentary canal the satisfaction felt in the taking of food, and in opposition to the digestive process goes a terrible stream of fear that comes from elemental spirits.

This is what animals leave behind them when they die. When animals die—not those species, perhaps, that I have already described in another context but nevertheless including some four-footed mammals for instance—when these animals die there also dies, or rather comes to life in their dying, a being which is entirely composed of anxiety. With the animal's death, fear is released, comes to life. In the case of beasts of prey, this fear is actually part of their enjoyment of the food. The beast of prey, which tears its prey to pieces, devours the flesh with satisfaction. And towards this satisfaction in the consumption of meat there streams fear, the fear which the herbivorous animal only gives off when it dies, but which already streams out from the beast of prey during its lifetime. The astral bodies of such animals as lions and tigers are therefore riddled with fear which they do not feel during their lifetime but which after death these animals drive back because it runs counter to their feeling of satisfaction. Thus carnivorous animals have an after-life in their group soul which must be said to be a much more terrible kamaloka than anything which can be experienced by the human being, and this simply on account of their intrinsic nature.

Naturally you must regard these things as being experienced in quite a different consciousness. If you took the materialistic view again, and began to imagine what the beast of prey must experience by putting yourself in its place, thinking, 'What would such a kamaloka be like for me?' and were then to judge the beast of prey according to what such a kamaloka might be for you, then you are of course materialistic, indeed animalistic, for you transpose yourself into animal nature. These things must of course be understood if one is to comprehend the world. But we must not put ourselves, with the consciousness we have, in their place, as when the materialist puts himself and the whole world into the category of lifeless matter.

This brings us to something about which I can only speak on a soul level, for anthroposophy should never campaign for anything, should never advocate either one thing or another, but should only present the truth. The conclusions people draw for their own lives are their own personal affair. Anthroposophy does not lay down rules, but puts forward truths. For this reason I shall never, even for fanatics, lay down any kind of law based on what an animal produces from its plant food. No dogmatic commands shall be given with regard to vegetarianism, meat-eating and so on, for these things must be a matter of personal judgement entirely and it is really only in the sphere of individual experience that they have value. I mention this in order to avoid giving people the idea that anthroposophy entails advocating this or that kind of diet. What it actually does is enable people to understand any form of diet.

What I really wished to show was that we must work on the mineral until it becomes warmth ether in order that it may absorb the spiritual; then, after the mineral has absorbed the spiritual, the human being can be built up by it. I mentioned that when the human being is still very young he does not yet have the strength to work on what is entirely mineral and convert it into warmth ether. Some of the work has been done for him when he drinks milk. Milk has already undergone preliminary changes that make the process of transformation to warmth ether easier. In a child the milk with its forces flows up quickly into the head and can there give rise to form-developing impulses in a way that the child can make use of, for the whole organization of the child proceeds from the head.

If at a later age the human being wishes to retain these form-developing forces, it is not good to promote them by drinking milk. In the case of the child, what ascends into the head is able by means of the forces of the head (which are present until the change of teeth) to radiate form principles into the whole body; in an older person the process is no longer present. In later age, the whole of the rest of the organism must radiate form-giving forces. And these form-giving forces for the whole organism are particularly strengthened in their impulses when one eats something which works in quite another way than is the case with the head.

You see, the head is entirely enclosed. Within this head are the impulses used in childhood for the shaping of the body. In the rest of the body we have bones within and the form-giving forces outside, so that the form-developing forces must be stimulated from outside. While we are children these form-giving forces in the head are stimulated when we give milk to the human being. When we are no longer children these forces are no longer there. What should we do then so that these form-giving forces may be stimulated more from outside?

It would obviously be a good thing to be able to have in our outer form what is accomplished within by the head, enclosed as it is inside the skull. It would be good if what the head does inside itself could be accomplished from somewhere outside. The forces which are there within the head are suited to the consumption of milk; when the milk is there in its etheric transformation it provides a good basis for the development of these head forces. We therefore ought to have something that acts like milk but is not produced within the human being, is instead produced from outside.

Well, there is something existing outside in nature which is a head without an enclosing skull and in which the same forces act from outside that work inside the head in children who need milk and must even create it anew (the child must first bring milk into the warmth-etheric condition and so create it anew).

A stock of bees is really a head open on all sides. What the bees are doing is actually the same as what the head does within itself. The hive we give them is at most a support. The bees' activity, however, is not enclosed but produced from outside. In a stock of bees we have under external spiritual influence the same thing as we have under spiritual influence inside the head. We have honey inside the beehive and when we eat and enjoy honey it gives us the form-giving forces that must now be provided more from outside, with the same strength and power that milk gives us for our head during the years of childhood.

Thus while we are still children we consume milk to strengthen the form-giving forces in a process that comes from the head. If at a later age we still need form-giving forces we must eat honey. Nor do we need to eat it in tremendous quantities—it is only a question of absorbing its forces.

Thus by fully understanding the outer world of nature one learns how forces that help development must be introduced into human life. And if we would conceive a land where there are beautiful children and beautiful old people, what kind of a land would this be? It would be 'a land flowing with milk and honey'. So you see ancient instinctive vision was in no way wrong when it said that the lands people longed for were those flowing with milk and honey.

Many such simple sayings contain the profoundest wisdom and there is really no more beautiful experience than first to make every possible effort to experience the truth, and then to find some ancient holy saying abounding in deep wisdom, such as 'a land flowing with milk and honey'. That is indeed a rare land, for in it there are only beautiful children and beautiful old people.

You see, to understand the human being presupposes understanding the world of nature. To understand the world of nature provides the basis for the understanding of the human being. And here the lowest spheres of the material always lead up to the highest spheres of the spiritual: the kingdoms of nature—mineral, animal, vegetable—at the one, the lowest pole; above, at the other pole, the hierarchies themselves.

3. Nutrition from a Cosmic Perspective

This lecture widens the ideas set out in the previous chapter to include not just plants but other types of food in their cosmic context. It then goes on to discuss the effects of various foods on physical and spiritual components of the human being.

It is interesting to compare three kinds of food in relation to their cosmic significance. First, there is milk and its products; second, there are plants and the foods prepared from them; and finally, there is nourishment through the use of animal products. We can begin to compare milk, plant and animal as nutrients when we have learned, through esoteric development, to distinguish their effects within the human organism. It is then easier to confirm the statements that arise from a rational observation of the material world. Occult observation of the cosmos reveals that milk substance can be found on earth, but not on any other planet in our solar system. What is produced in a similar manner in the organism of living beings on other planets in our solar system would be something totally different from terrestrial milk. Milk is unique to the earthly realm. If we wanted to generalize about milk, we would have to say that the beings inhabiting each planetary system have their own particular milk.

When we examine the plant system of earth and compare it from an esoteric perspective with the plant systems of other planets—that is, with what corresponds to plant systems on other planets—we could say that the plant forms on earth are different from those on other planets of our solar system. Yet the inner nature of the plants on earth does not derive merely from earthly existence. The inner nature of plants belongs in the context of the solar system—that is, plant nature on earth is connected to the nature of plants on other planets of our solar system. There is an element in our plants that can be found also on other planets in our solar system.

As for the animal kingdom, it follows from what I said about milk that the animal kingdom on earth—and this can easily be demonstrated from an occult perspective—is radically different from any corresponding kingdom on other planets. If we take the effect of milk as nutrient for the human body, nourishment from milk demonstrates to the esotericist that milk is, so to speak, not just the element that binds the human body to earth, but also the element that brings the body together with the human species on earth as belonging to a common genus. That humankind, in relation to the physical system of human components, also constitutes a whole is because of the fact that milk as a living nutrient provides sustenance for living beings of animal provenance. Everything that milk supplies to the human organism prepares an individual to be a human creature of earth, placed within earthly circumstances, and yet not actually confined to earth. It makes the human being a citizen of the earth, but does not prevent someone from being at the same time a citizen of the entire solar system.

With regard to animal foods, the situation is different. Meat is derived from a domain that is specifically earth-bound. But meat, unlike milk, is not obtained directly from the life processes of the living being, human or animal. Meat is obtained from the part of animal substance that has already been prepared for the animal. Such food binds the human being directly to the earth; it makes the human being into an earthbound creature. Therefore we must say that in so far as human beings permeate their organism with the effects of nutrition derived from meat they are deprived of the forces that could free them from the earth. By eating a meat diet, we bind ourselves in the most direct and intimate sense to the planet earth. Whereas milk enables us to participate as 'members' of the earthly realm undergoing a temporary stage in the process of human development, eating animal foods condemns us (unless we are raised to a higher stage by some other means) to make the earthly sojourn into a permanent one, within which we are completely bound to conform. The decision to consume milk products is like saying, 'I wish to remain on earth in order to be able to fulfil my task there, but do not wish to dwell there permanently.' The tendency to eat meat, on the other hand, is like saying, 'Life on earth appeals to me so much that I renounce the joys of heaven, because I prefer to be wholly absorbed in the conditions of earthly existence.' A vegetarian diet stimulates the forces in the human organism that bring us into a kind of cosmic union with the whole planetary system. When in the course of accomplishing our daily tasks we transform plant nutrients in our organism, we activate forces contained in the whole solar system. As a result, we participate through our physical components in the forces that inhabit the solar system; we do not become alienated or detached from them. This is something that the soul, as it develops anthroposophically or esoterically, gradually experiences within itself. In other words, we have the experience that through taking in plant nutrients the soul is assimilating something that does not possess earthly weight, but belongs rather to the sun, that is, to the central body of the entire planetary system. The lightness of the organism resulting from a vegetarian diet lifts one above earthly heaviness and makes possible what one might call a gradual responsiveness that develops into a certain inner perception of taste in the human organism. It is as though, under the influence of a vegetarian diet, our organism really shared with the plants the sunlight that contributes so much to their growth and flowering.

You will gather from what I have said that it is extremely important for occult, esoteric development not to bind oneself, as it were, to the earth by taking into oneself earthly 'heaviness' by consuming animal food. Those on the path of esoteric development, then, should avoid animal food to the extent that individual and hereditary circumstances permit. The ultimate decision, however, must depend on the personal circumstances of the individual. It will certainly be of real assistance to the whole development of a person's life if meat consumption can be avoided. On the other hand, certain difficulties might arise if one were to become a fanatical vegetarian, rejecting milk and all milk products. In this case, the soul's spiritual development could encounter certain dangers because, by rejecting milk and milk products, we easily develop a love solely for what detaches us from the earth, and thus we would lose the threads that unite us with earthly human activities.

I should stress that, in a certain sense, it is a good thing if anthroposophical seekers do not move towards fanatical spiritual enthusiasm and thus create an obstacle in their physical bodies that would separate them from any relationship to what is earthly and human. In order not to become too eccentric in the pursuit of soul development—in order not to be alienated from human feeling and human impulses on earth—it is good, as pilgrims on earth, to allow ourselves, to a certain extent, to take on 'ballast', as it were, by consuming milk and milk products. In a way, it can be a kind of training not just to live in the spiritual world and so become estranged from earth, but also to have tasks to fulfil on earth. It can be a systematic training not to be a strict vegetarian, but to take milk and milk products as well. Our organism, the physical body, will then be related to humankind and the earth without being bound to it or burdened with the earthbound nature that occurs in the case of meat consumption.

It is interesting to see how these things are related to cosmic mysteries and how, through knowledge of these cosmic mysteries, we can follow the actual effect of nutritional substances in the human organism. Since you are interested in esoteric truths, you must have become aware that what we find on earth—and our physical body is an integral part of earthly existence—does not derive from earthly conditions alone, but arises also from the forces and conditions of essential existence imbedded in supra-earthly and cosmic nature.

This happens in a very specific way. Take, for example, the protein present in a hen's egg. We must understand clearly that this animal protein is not just what chemists find in their analyses, but that this protein, in its structure, results from cosmic forces. Basically, these cosmic forces work on the protein only after they have first acted on the earth and, above all, on the moon that accompanies earth. The cosmic influences on the protein are therefore indirect; they first act on the earth which, in turn, reacts to the composition of the protein with the forces that it receives from the cosmos. Above all, however, it is the moon that plays the major part, in the sense that the moon first receives the forces from the cosmos and then, with the forces that it radiates, works on the composition of animal protein. Someone endowed with clairvoyant vision can see in the smallest cell of the animal—and thus also in protein—that not just terrestrial physical, chemical forces are present, but also that even the smallest cell of a hen's egg is built from forces received by the earth from the cosmos; thus the substance we call protein is indirectly connected with the cosmos. Nevertheless, this animal protein substance, as we know it on earth, could not exist without earthly conditions; it could not originate directly out of the cosmos but is wholly a product of what the earth must receive from the cosmos.

What we identify in living beings on earth as fat—which constitutes a part of human nutrition, especially for those who eat meat—has a different effect. Here we are speaking of fatty substance in the animal. What we call fat, whether it is eaten or manufactured by one's body, is built up according to cosmic laws entirely different from those related to protein formation. Whereas the cosmic forces of the beings who are the spirits of form are concerned with protein, those beings called spirits of movement are mainly concerned with the production of the fatty substance.

It is important to speak of such matters, because only by discussing them in this way can we recognize how very complicated those things are that material science considers so infinitely simple. No living being could assimilate either protein or fat without the cooperation (even if indirectly) of the cosmos—that is, the spirits of form and the spirits of movement.* Thus we can trace the spiritual effects of the

---

* Regarding these spirit beings, see *An Outline of Occult Science*, especially the chapter 'The Evolution of the Cosmos and Man'; see also *The Spiritual Hierarchies and the Physical World: Reality and Illusion* (Anthroposophic Press, Hudson, NY 1996).

activity of the different hierarchies right into the substance that makes up our physical bodies. This is why what we experience in relation to the protein and fat substance in our physical components when the soul has developed anthroposophically becomes more differentiated, more mobile. We experience this in a twofold way. What merges into a single experience in ordinary human life is experienced, after we have undergone anthroposophical development, as the differentiated activity of the fats and proteins in our organism.

As the whole physical organism becomes more mobile, the soul learns to distinguish two different experiences within the body. One experience permeates us inwardly to the degree that we feel: 'This puts me together, this gives me my physical form.' In this way we are made aware of the proteins within us. When a certain indifference is added to our own experience, when we feel, 'This makes me indifferent to my inner isolation, lifts me, as it were, above my form, and makes me more phlegmatic in relation to my inner human feeling,' this sluggish feeling reflects the presence of fat substance in the physical body. These experiences become very distinct because of anthroposophical development. Our inner experience in relation to the physical body thus becomes more complex.

We perceive this particularly in the case of starches or sugar. In this regard, sugar is unique because it is differentiated from other substances through its taste, and this can be experienced clearly in ordinary life, not just by children but frequently also in elderly people who have a sweet tooth. However, such differentiation is usually restricted to the palate. When the soul develops, it experiences the intake of sugar and the body's sugar content as though receiving inner stability, inner support, and it is permeated to a certain extent with a kind of natural ego-character. In this respect, one can extol the virtues of sugar. In fact, in the process of spiritual development one often notices a need for sugar, because through development the soul aims to become progressively more selfless; through sound anthroposophical training, the soul through its own effort becomes more selfless. Thus in order that a human being—who by virtue of possessing a physical body has an earthly task to fulfil—does not lose the link between the I and the earth, it is good to create a counterpoise in the physical domain where ego-character is not as important as it is in the moral sphere. Eating sugar creates a kind of 'innocent ego-character', as it were, that can balance the selflessness necessary in the moral and spiritual spheres. Otherwise, the human being would be tempted too easily to become not just selfless, but also a dreamer and visionary and thus lose the capacity for sound judgement in mundane affairs. Adding a certain amount of sugar to one's food ensures the possibility of remaining anchored firmly to the earth, and one thus cultivates a healthy perspective towards earthly matters, even while ascending into the spiritual world. (As you see, these matters are complicated; but when we seek to penetrate life's real mysteries, everything becomes complicated!)

As anthroposophists develop spiritually, they sometimes feel that in order to protect against a false selflessness, or a loss of personality, they sometimes need more sugar. And when taking sugar they may say, 'I am adding something to myself that, without lowering my moral tone, gives me a certain stability, a certain ego-character as though involuntarily and through a higher instinct.' On the whole, we can say that eating sugar physically enhances the unique individuality of a person. We can be so sure of this that we can say,

'Those who favour sweets (of course, this must be kept within healthy limits) find it easier to imprint their personal character into their physical body than those who dislike sweets.' This can help us to understand something that may be observed outwardly. In countries where, according to statistics, sugar consumption is low, the inhabitants have less defined personalities than in countries where more sugar is eaten. If you visit countries where the people show greater individuality, where each individual is self-aware, and then go to countries where the inhabitants have more general, or homogeneous, characteristics—even showing less individuality in their outward appearance—you will discover that in the former countries sugar consumption is high, in the latter very low.

Even more striking examples of food's effects can be seen when we consider those of certain stimulants, for example the consumption of coffee and tea in significant amounts. The effect of consuming coffee or tea for an ordinary person is intensified in a person undergoing anthroposophical development. As I have said, this is not an argument for or against coffee, but simply a statement of how it is, and I ask you to view it from that perspective. Coffee and tea stimulate the constitution of ordinary human beings, but the stimulating effect of coffee and tea on the human organism is felt more keenly by a soul developing spiritually. The effect of coffee on the human organism is to lift the etheric body out of the physical body, but in such a way that the physical body is experienced as a solid foundation for the etheric body; this is the characteristic effect of coffee. The physical body is differentiated from the etheric body in such a way that—especially in terms of its form—it is experienced as radiating into the etheric body as a kind of solid foundation for the etheric body's experiences when influenced by coffee. This must not be taken as a defence for drinking coffee, because all of this occurs on the physical plane, and we would become completely dependent if we wanted to prepare ourselves spiritually by using such stimulants. We are only characterizing the influence of these stimulants. However, because logical, consistent thinking arises from the structure and form of the physical body, the characteristic effect of coffee emphasizes the physical structure and physically promotes logical consistency. Drinking coffee physically furthers logical consistency—that is, consistent thinking based on facts. And although it may be injurious to health to drink large amounts of coffee, for those who wish to rise to spiritual heights it is not especially harmful. It may occasionally be good to have recourse to the stimulation of coffee in order to promote logical consistency. It seems quite natural that the professional writer who cannot quite find the logical sequence from one sentence to the next and who chews a pencil searching for inspiration would turn to coffee for stimulation. Anyone who knows how to penetrate to the veiled, or esoteric, foundation of these things can easily understand this. Even though, as earthly citizens, we sometimes need this drink according to individual circumstances, let me emphasize that coffee, despite its dangers to health, can contribute greatly towards reinforcing stability. Not that it should be recommended as a means to this end, but it can promote stability. And when, for example, the beginner is inclined to let thoughts stray in the wrong direction, we need not take it amiss if such a person tries to achieve greater stability by drinking coffee.

Tea is a different matter. Its effect is analogous to coffee, that is, a kind of differentiation between the physical nature and the etheric nature, but here the structure of the physical body is neutralized, or 'disconnected', and the tendency of the etheric body to fluctuate is emphasized. As a result of drinking tea, thoughts become dissociated, unstable, less capable of sticking to facts. Tea, in fact, stimulates imagination, but not always in a very appealing way; it does not make for fidelity to truth or for accommodation to the reality of circumstances. It is understandable, therefore, that in social gatherings where great value is placed on flashes of wit and intellectual virtuosity, the stimulation is readily provided by tea. On the other hand, it is also understandable that when tea drinking becomes an excessive habit, it engenders a certain indifference towards the demands of a healthy physical, earthly body. Thus dreamy fantasy as well as a certain nonchalant apathy that ignores the demands of a solid exoteric life are easily encouraged by tea drinking. The soul does not favour tea while developing spiritually because tea drinking leads more easily to pretence than coffee drinking. Spiritual development works towards greater stability, whereas tea encourages greater charlatanism (though these characterizations are extreme). These things, as we have said, can all be experienced because of the mobility that anthroposophical training brings to the human physical component.

I would like here to add (and you can meditate further on these things or try to experience them personally) that if coffee drinking promotes something like stability in the physical body and if tea drinking favours charlatanism, then chocolate mainly promotes philistinism. When the physical body becomes more mobile, it is possible that we can recognize chocolate as the beverage of the ordinary, the everyday, through direct experience. Chocolate can be

recommended for festivities and it is very understandable—
excuse the aside—that at family festivals, christenings,
birthday celebrations, especially in certain circles on festive
occasions, chocolate is the customary beverage.

If we remember that all of these beverages are stimulants,
their influence assumes a greater significance. This is
because our normal experience of food influences our
ordinary daily life in such a way that we are not merely aware
of the fundamental substance that builds and constantly
renews the body, but we also become aware, as mentioned
yesterday, of the inner independence, or the dissociation, of
the organs from one another. This is important and very
significant.

4. Nutrition and the Human Body

We now move from the cosmic aspects of nutrition to the effect which various food categories, such as protein, carbohydrates and fats, have on the various components of the human body. Under this heading, Rudolf Steiner discusses topics ranging from the processes in the stomach to hangovers.

I'd like to add something to what I said last Saturday. I can answer the two questions I have been given for today the next time. We have been speaking of poisons and their actions on human beings, and have learned from those poisons that for genuine knowledge we must rise to the supersensory aspect, to the spiritual aspects of the human being.

Today I'd like to complete the picture and add something to the discussion of elements that have such powerful poisonous effects. This concerns the work done by a more or less healthy body in nutrition. I have spoken on nutrition on a number of occasions, but let us speak again of some aspects relating to nutrition, taking into account what was said the last time.

To feed himself, the human being mainly takes in three or four kinds of foods. The first is protein, which you can get to know most easily by looking at a hen's egg. Protein is produced in plants as well as in animal and human bodies. Both human and animal bodies need not only the powers they have in them to produce protein, for every living body actually produces protein; they also need the protein which a plant produces quite independently. And the human body also takes in animal protein. Some scientists have suffered severe embarrassment very recently concerning this very protein. Twenty years ago it was still taught everywhere that people had to consume at least 120 grams of protein a day to stay healthy. The whole of nutrition was therefore geared to it that dishes were recommended which people should eat in order to have the right amount of protein; 120 grams were thought to be necessary.

Today scientists have completely abandoned that idea. They know that people do not serve their health by eating so much protein but actually serve their ill-health, with the greater part of the protein going putrid in the human intestinal organism. Consuming 120 grams of protein a day, therefore, the human organism constantly has something like rotting eggs in its gut, polluting the intestinal contents most dreadfully, sweating out poisons which then enter into the organism, into the body. This not only produces something in the body that later on in life causes hardening of the arteries, as it is called—most of this comes from eating too much protein—but also making people highly susceptible to infection with all kinds of infectious diseases. Given that they must, of course, have the necessary amount, people are less at risk of catching infectious diseases the less excess protein they consume. Anyone taking at lot of protein will more easily catch infectious diseases—diphtheria, smallpox—than someone who does not take in so much protein.

It is strange indeed that scientists are now saying people do not need 120 grams of protein but only 20 to 50 grams. This, they say, is the amount people really need every day. So quickly have scientists changed their views in two decades. So you see how much store you may set by anything said to have been scientifically established. For if it should happen that you need to find out about the subject and you take a 20-year-old encyclopedia, you will read in the relevant chapter that you should have 120 grams of protein. If you consulted a later edition you would read: 20 to 50 grams, and that it will make you ill to take more. So you see how it is, basically, with scientific truths. You are informed what you should consider to be true or false, depending on the edition of the encyclopedia you consult.

All this shows that this simply is not the way to get a clear picture about things that involve the spiritual dimension.

And it gives us reason, if we really think about it, to enter into the spiritual aspects if we want to understand what happens when people consume protein. But this is the food that absolutely must still be processed in the intestines, in the abdomen, and the abdomen itself must have the power to digest this protein. You know that protein, especially fresh egg white, is semi-fluid. All protein is semi-fluid. Anything semi-fluid is accessible to the human etheric body. The human etheric body cannot do anything with solid matter, only with fluid matter. Human beings must therefore take all the food they consume in fluid form.

You will say that when people take salt, sugar, or the like, they are solid. Yes, but they are immediately dissolved. That is why we have saliva. The solid matter of which the actual physical body is made must never come into the human body from the outside world. From this you may learn: you have solid matter in you. You know that. Your bones are solid. But it is like this: the solid bones are created out of the fluid element in the human body; no solid from the outside world can ever enter into the human body. The human body must let all its solid parts arise out of the fluid sphere. You are thus able to say: we have solid matter in us and this is our physical body, but the physical body is wholly and entirely created out of the fluid sphere, and for the fluid sphere we have the etheric body, a subtle body that cannot be seen but is present everywhere in the human being.

Protein must also be completely converted by the etheric body, and this happens in the abdomen. The higher aspects of the human being are also active there, as I have told you, but the protein must be processed in the etheric body. The fluid sphere thus exists for the human etheric body. And by merely knowing that protein has to be converted in the lower human body, you are able to realize that protein cannot have the hardest task in the human being, for it does not have to act up into the chest, it does not have to work up into the human head. You can see from this that protein cannot be a food of prime importance. We may say that people cannot possibly eat too little protein, for it is processed immediately in the abdomen; it does not have to do much work. Protein is processed in the abdomen. Even if people have a diet that is very low in protein, all the protein is processed immediately.

We can see, therefore, that human beings are perfectly able to manage with little protein. Scientists will now admit this, but years ago children in particular were fed excessive amounts of protein. And you know we see those children who in the 1870s and 1880s were given too much protein going about with hardening of the arteries, or they have already died of hardening of the arteries. The harmfulness of something does not show immediately, it only shows itself much later.

The second kind of foods are the fats. The fats we eat will of course also reach the abdomen. But fats pass through the intestines and act most strongly on the middle human body, on the chest. For the middle body, the chest region, for proper nutrition of the heart, chest, and so on, it is therefore absolutely necessary to take in fatty substances.

We see from this that human beings above all need fatty substances in the chest region because that is the region where we breathe. What does this mean? It means that carbon, which we have in us, combines with oxygen. When carbon combines with oxygen we need to supply heat. What the fats do, when they themselves combine with oxygen, is to produce heat. Fats therefore contribute a great deal specifically to what is needed in the chest region.

Now we may say that proteins have a tendency to putrefy if they are not processed in the body, in the abdomen. To have proteins in us that cannot be properly digested actually means that we have something like rotten eggs in our gut. I think you know the stink of rotten eggs, gentlemen, and the situation is that when people take too much protein they sweat out this stink of rotten eggs into their internal organism. They fill themselves with this stink of rotten eggs. If you leave eggs for some time they become rotten eggs, and they stink like rotten eggs. And the part that has not been digested in the body will of course also produce a stink in the body; the other part, which is digested, will not produce a stink but enter cleanly into the body. And that is the work of the etheric body. The etheric body exists to overcome and remove the rotten stink that develops. The way it is in the human body is that the etheric body fights and overcomes the rotting process. The rotting process is overcome by the etheric body in the human being. When a human being no longer has an etheric body after death, he begins to rot away. So there you have it right in front of your nose, we might say, that a human being does not rot away while he is alive; as soon as he no longer lives, he rots. Why is that so? Because the etheric body has gone when a person is dead. The etheric body is therefore the part of the human being that prevents rotting. We therefore have a continuous battle going on inside us against rotting away, and it is the etheric body which fights that battle in us.

I think, gentlemen, you only need to think this through and you'll see very clearly, just from the evidence of your eyes, that there must be an etheric body, that in fact there has to be an etheric body everywhere. For proteins are produced everywhere on earth, and they rot. The earth would have to stink to high heaven if the ether did not keep driving this rotting principle away. Both inside and outside the human organism, the ether fights against proteins going rotten all the time. This is something we must certainly consider.

When we come to the fats, we have to say that fats do not rot but go rancid. You all know this, if you have ever left fats somewhere outside; even butter will go rancid. Fats thus have the property of going rancid. Now if you have left butter to stand, you will not be able to say if it is rancid or good fresh butter unless you have developed an eye for it. But when you taste it on your tongue you will know right away that it is rancid. This has something to do with awareness, therefore, with sensation. Rotting has to do with our sense of smell, with something you can smell outside. It is different, of course, if you have rotten eggs or the scent of roses, but in either case you smell it. Not so if something goes rancid. Going rancid is something where we only put a name to it because of something more inward, our sense of taste.

This immediately shows that it has a lot more to do with an inner response than in the case of eggs going rotten. The middle human body, the chest, has to do with everything that is an inner response coming to awareness; and spiritually it is the astral body. As you know, in the chest we have something that functions on an airy principle. We breathe in air. We transform air. The air has its rightful place in the chest. In the remaining part of the human body gases and types of air should only be produced sparingly. If too much gas is produced in the gut, pathological flatulence develops, and that is not healthy. The middle human body exists for the generation of gases. And the higher supersensory spiritual aspect which intervenes here—it intervenes in things that are gaseous by nature—is the human astral body. This fights the going rancid of fats in itself. Just as the etheric body combats the rotting of proteins, so the astral body combats the going rancid of fats. People would continually have rancid eructations from their own fats, they would taste rancid to themselves inwardly, if their astral bodies did not constantly fight this process of going rancid. We thus have this astral body inside us to prevent fats going rancid.

You see, gentlemen, this is truly marvellous, for you can see from this that things go very differently in the ordinary physical world outside than they do inside us. Out there in the physical world fats inevitably go rancid. Human beings are blessed in that they do not go rancid, or only if they develop an internal disease. The matter is, therefore, that in health human beings have their astral body so that they cannot go rancid. They only go rancid if they eat too much fat, so that the astral body is unable to cope, or if something or other causes too much fat to be produced; cannibals know more about this than we do. Inwardly, however, human beings do perceive it if they go rancid. We may say that if someone grows very rancid, which means that his astral body is not sufficiently active, he continually has an unpleasant taste in his mouth. This unpleasant taste in turn affects the stomach. And in this roundabout way people get diseases of the stomach and intestines from the rancid fat in them.

If you notice that a person is inwardly going rancid, then arsenic is a good medicine for fats he has inside him which are not digested. Arsenic prevents one getting fat; it strengthens the astral body. The result is that a person is then able to combat the process of going rancid. These things are extraordinarily important. When a person shows himself to have an inner tendency of being unable to overcome his rotting protein with the help of the etheric body, some copper compound or other usually proves highly effective as a medicine. Copper is thus effective when abdominal diseases, intestinal diseases are caused directly by protein. But when you find that something comes to awareness in the mouth, in the taste, it will not help to give copper; in that case it has to be arsenic, because you must first of all strengthen the astral body. It will not do to say simply that diseases of one kind or another are in a particular part of the human being. You have to know where they come from, if they come from rotting protein in the gut or fats that have gone rancid and affect the intestines and the stomach via the taste in one's mouth.

You see, therefore, gentlemen, that inside us we have the opposite of what these substances show themselves to be on the outside. We have an astral body that combats the going rancid of fats, while the ordinary physical and material world simply makes fats go rancid.

A third food people eat consists of the substances known as carbohydrates. Carbohydrates are found particularly in potatoes, for instance, in lentils and beans, and of course in all cereal grains. The carbohydrates are in there. Very many of them also contain actual sugar, which we always take as a

food, or the sugar is directly produced from those carbohydrates because we transform the substances we take in
when we eat potatoes, for instance. Potatoes contain much
starch. This sticky starch is converted to dextrin inside us and
then into sugar. If you eat potatoes you are therefore really
taking sugar, for the potato starch paste is converted to sugar
in the human body. As you know, grapes are particularly rich
in sugar, hence also the alcohol. Everything that alcohol is to
the human being is, apart from being alcohol, really due to its
sugar content, for sugar is produced particularly from alcohol
in the human organism.

The first kind of food thus was protein, the second kind
fats and the third starch, sugar. We have seen that protein is
digested in certain quantities, without going putrid, by the
etheric body. Fats are digested, without going rancid, by the
astral body. Now to starch and sugar. Looking at the etheric
body we have to say it is mainly active in the abdomen. The
astral body is mainly active in the chest region. Now we come
to something else. You all know—I won't say from personal
experience, but from seeing people who are not like you—the
effects of alcohol, and you know that alcohol causes a
peculiar condition in people, first of all drunkenness, but
we'll leave that aside for the moment. But as you know, the
next day one has a thick head, a hangover. What does such a
heavy head or hangover signify?

Well, gentlemen, you can see even the term 'thick head'
refers to the human head. And if you have heard people—
different from yourselves, of course—talk about the bit of a
hangover they had the day before, you will hear them com-
plain above all of their skulls. The skull aches, and if it did not
ache it felt as if it would drop off their shoulders, and so on.
What is really going on?

The function of the head is to combat what starch and sugar want. What do starch and sugar want? You only have to consider wine. As you know, the wine, the grapes, are harvested when autumn comes. They are pressed and the matter then ferments. When fermentation is complete, people drink the wine. By becoming wine through fermentation, wine has overcome the fermentation. But if you put wine into your stomach, something develops from it that becomes part of the food again. The alcohol is literally converted back. Now starch and sugar are substances that want to ferment. Starch and sugar mainly want to ferment in the human organism. If you drink alcohol, the alcohol drives away the powers in the head that prevent the fermentation of sugar and starch in the human being. Let us take a good look at this. Let us say you had potatoes on 22 January, you had some beans and you drank alcohol with them. Right then. If you had not taken alcohol your head would have remained sober. Potatoes and beans contain starch and the sugar that comes from starch. The head would have the power to prevent fermentation of the starch and sugar in the proper way. If you bring in alcohol, the head loses the ability to prevent the fermentation of the starch and sugar you have in you from the potatoes, and then the potatoes and beans, and other things, too, cereal grains, for example, begin to ferment inside you.

Instead of being prevented, fermentation occurs in the person. It occurs because of the inability of the head that has developed because of the alcohol, so that the person comes to be full of fermentative powers. In central Germany, in Thuringia, people have a strange popular expression. When someone talks nonsense, people in Thuringia say: 'He ferments.' It is not something people say in this area, but those who have been to Germany will no doubt have heard it in

central Germany. And when someone is talking nonsense all
the time, people in central Germany, in Thuringia, call him
'an old wretch in ferment'. The situation is that in central
Germany people connect fermentation with confusion in the
head, with fooling around. That is an excellent popular
instinct. They know that when someone talks a lot of nonsense he is in ferment in his head. And if someone has been
drinking and got a thick head, he does not talk nonsense, for
he tends to be quiet, but the nonsense is inside him, it
rumbles in him. The process which develops to prevent the
fermentation of starch and sugar is therefore the opposite of
the tangible effect of alcohol. We may say, therefore, that
there is something in the human head that continually works
in the direction of preventing the fermentation of everything
the person has in him by way of starch and sugar.

No one will deny that the I, the human I as such, has its
main seat in the head, just as the etheric body has its seat
in the lower part and the astral body in the middle part of
the human body. The situation is that this I has to do with
warmth qualities, just as the physical body has to do with
solids, the etheric body with fluids and the astral body with
gases. The situation is that with everything that relates to
his I the human being makes warmth move. This can be
seen in detail if we study the human body. The I is also
connected with the blood, and the blood therefore produces warmth. But the I, of which human beings have conscious awareness, is also connected with glandular
secretion, for instance. Because of this, glandular secretion
is connected with temperature conditions. With its supersensory powers the I also uses the powers of the head to
prevent fermentation. We are thus able to say: the etheric
body combats the rotting of proteins, the astral body com-

bats fats going rancid, and the I combats the fermentation of sugar and starch.

This is also the reason why I had to tell you on one occasion that eating too many potatoes is bad for the head. Excessive potato consumption affects the human being as follows. You see, a potato contains little protein, which basically makes it a good human food. And if people eat moderate amounts of potatoes together with other things, the potato is a good food, having little protein. But it contains an extraordinary amount of starch which has to be converted to sugar in the human being, first into dextrin and then into sugar. I told you on that earlier occasion that the head has to do a terrible lot of work when people eat too many potatoes, obviously, for the head has to prevent fermentation. People who eat too many potatoes and have to make a terrible effort in their heads to cope with potato fermentation therefore tend to be weak in the head. It is mainly the middle parts of the brain that grow weak, leaving only the front parts which make little effort to prevent potato fermentation. It is actually due to the fact that potatoes have come to be widely eaten in recent times that materialism has developed, for this is produced in the front part of the brain.

It is really peculiar. People think materialism is a matter of logic. To some extent materialism is nothing but the consequence of eating potatoes! Now I think you'll agree people do not really like it if they have to live mainly on potatoes, but they do like materialism. So they are really caught up in a contradiction. To be a proper materialist, one should really advise everyone to eat potatoes, for that would surely be the best way of being convinced of materialism. But it is something that does not happen with most people ...

One thing you can see from this is that the science of the

spirit we work with here recognizes the true nature of materialism. Materialism does not know anything about the world of matter; the science of the spirit recognizes the potato in particular as the real creator of materialism. It is dreadfully malicious, the potato, crafty, sly to an excessive degree. For you see, people can only eat the tubers of potatoes, not even the eyes on a potato—they are harmful—and they certainly cannot eat the flowers, for the potato is a member of the deadly nightshade family and the flowers are poisonous. But what is poison? As I told you the last time, large amounts of a poison kill, small amounts, in fine distribution, are medicinal. Potato as such contains much sticky starch, it consists almost entirely of sticky starch. It would be quite unable to live, because the sticky starch would be terribly harmful to it. But it attracts poison from the world at the same time, and destroys the harmful effect that is inside itself. This is why I say it is crafty and sly. It has its poison which removes the effect that would be harmful to it. But the poison in potatoes is particularly harmful to humans; it does not give this ability to them but only the matter which it renders harmless in itself by using the poison. This really is something we may refer to by saying that the potato is a sly, crafty thing. And people must clearly understand that if they eat too many potatoes their midbrain will wither away and it is even possible that their senses also suffer from eating too many potatoes.

If someone eats too many potatoes as a child or a young person, his midbrain will become extraordinarily weak. But the midbrain is the source of the most important sense organs. In the midbrain lie four rounded eminences called colliculi, the thalamus, and so on, and excessive potato consumption even weakens one's eyesight, for this has its origins in the midbrain. Some eye conditions in old age are due to the person having been brought up eating too many potatoes as a child. A person then gets weak eyes, weak eyesight. It really is true that people in Europe suffered much less from weak eyesight in earlier times than they do now. And this is because apart from other things that influence the eyes (but less strongly, because they do not act from inside, electric light and so on) excessive potato consumption in particular is very harmful to the eyes, affecting our vision and even the ability to taste—even the ability to taste! You see, the consequence is as follows. Let us assume someone eats too many potatoes even as a child. Later in life you will very often find that such a person never knows when he has had enough, because his sense of taste has been ruined by potato consumption, while someone who has not eaten too many potatoes will know instinctively when he has had enough. This instinct, which is largely connected with the midbrain, is thus ruined by excessive potato consumption. This is something that has emerged particularly clearly in recent times.

From everything I have said you will see that people must take particular care to be strong enough to overcome firstly the rotting of proteins, secondly the getting rancid of fats, thirdly the fermentation of starch and sugar.

As I told you the last time, people cannot be complete anti-alcoholics, for if they do not take any alcohol at all, alcohol is produced inside them. This alcohol stays in the abdomen; it does not go up to the head, for the head must be free from alcohol, otherwise it will be unable, as bearer of the I, to have proper control of the fermentation in the body. You see, you can now have an idea of the way in which human beings relate to their natural environment. Looking at rotting protein everywhere—animals rot away, plants rot away—you have to say: ether is also present everywhere, and this gradually balances it out again. Looking at fats, which are also found in plants, which are found everywhere, you have to say: these fats would gradually make it impossible for all living creatures to continue to live, both animals and humans, if the astral body were not present to combat the process of going rancid. The human being thus fights everything that exists in nature outside. And when the human being dies the etheric body, astral body and I depart. They leave the physical body. The human being then moves on into the world of the spirit. What happens then? Well, gentlemen, you know what happens. The dead body immediately begins to rot, to go rancid and at the same time to ferment, though the rotting is more apparent to the eye and to the nose, for we only rarely go about with our noses blocked up. The rotting process is thus easily smelt. But to go and lie across a grave somewhere and taste if the fat of the dead body has gone rancid—that is something we do not normally do, and therefore people usually do not know about it. And the fermentation that takes place is not studied at all. So it truly is the case that because the I departs the human body begins to ferment, because the astral body departs the human body goes rancid, and because the etheric body departs the human body starts to rot. This is something human beings always have in them, but for as long as they live on earth they are always fighting it. Anyone who denies that the etheric body, the astral body and the I are present in the body as real spiritual entities simply has to be asked: 'What do you imagine? Why does the human being not rot away? Why does he not ferment? Why does he not go rancid?' This would have to happen to the body if it were just a physical body.

What do our scientists do? They wait until a human being has died before they examine him. For they know precious little of the living human being compared to what they know of the anatomy of the dead body, when the human being has died. Everything you are able to learn from them really only relates to the dead body. Scientists always wait for the dead body. They are thus quite unable to know anything about the real human being, who is alive, for they do not consider him. And this is the great problem, that all the knowledge of our modern science—this really is only so since the seventeenth century—basically comes only from the dead body. But the dead body is no longer the human being, for we have to ask ourselves: what brings it about that the dead body which human beings have also when they are alive does not behave like the dead body, rotting, fermenting and going rancid? It is exactly when we take a real look at the living human being that we discover these supersensory aspects of human nature. And we then also find that the I is active mainly in the head, that the astral body is active mainly in the chest, and that the etheric body is active mainly in the abdomen. And scientists do not know anything about the abdomen, for they believe the processes in there are the same as those in outside nature. But that is not so.

Well, gentlemen, it is interesting to study things by not shutting oneself away in one's study but going out among living people. You know there are spas where you get a smell of rotten eggs, in Marienbad for instance, because the water contains hydrogen sulphide. Yes, really, people who like fine foods and are also fussy about smells have to go to such spas. And why do they go? Why do they sometimes spend several summer months in places where it smells as if there were rotten eggs everywhere? You see, it is like this. These people really have eaten too much protein and now come to the spa. They are covered with skin and the whole business is inside, and so they do not smell like that. But if we were able to smell it, they would smell horribly of rotten eggs inside. So all the people who inwardly smell of rotten eggs come to the spas where you get a smell of rotten eggs. And what happens? Well, you see, in one case the rotten egg smell is inside, and in the other it is outside. In the one case, where it is inside, the nose does not notice it; in the other case, where it is outside, the nose does notice. Head and belly are opposites. The rotten egg smell produced in the belly is combated when it comes from the head side, through the sense of smell. And the inner smell of rotten eggs is fought in spas that smell of rotten eggs.

This is very noticeable for anyone who is inclined to make such observations. It so happens that when I was a boy I had to go to such a spa. Every second day I had to go to a spring called Marienquelle. There you also get a smell of rotten eggs. While this is rather unpleasant outwardly, there being such a terrible smell, you suddenly begin to feel rather good in your belly. So if one is not sick, and does not have the rotten egg smell in one's belly, a feeling of greater vitality comes up. Anyone who is not driven away by the smell can experience this. Someone who holds his nose will of course not experience the contrast, will not have this springtime effect in the belly that comes if one really gives oneself up to the rotten egg smell. And rotten egg smell is an extraordinarily good medicine, for example, even if artificially produced. It will give the body the power to make atrophying muscles grow strong and firm again. People are not keen on such treatments, but in one respect they are extraordinarily useful. For you see, if the rotten egg smell comes to us from outside, spring comes inside, in the belly. And in spring everything grows and sprouts, and people can gain new strength when spring comes inside, in their bellies. This then is what happens with people who ruin their digestion by eating too much during the winter. You see, when someone does not ruin his digestion by eating too much in winter, he shares in the spring that comes in the outside world. The abdomen in particular participates in the spring very strongly. But if you want to really enjoy spring in the world of nature outside, you should as far as possible avoid such things as goose liver pâté and so on. If you have eaten a lot of goose liver pâté then the environment in your belly will always be the way it is below the surface of the soil in winter, not above ground but below ground. It is warm there, for it is where pits are dug to store potatoes through the winter. But it all goes rotten in the human being because the warmth is stored in the belly; spring does not come in the human being. And then he must find an artificial spring in the smell of rotten eggs.

This is the contrast between the I and etheric body. The I and etheric body must be in balance in the human being. You can see from this that if one really studies things in the world of nature, going to a spa that has the smell of rotten eggs with open senses, the sensation of spring in one's belly teaches one that inwardly the opposite process takes effect as proteins begin to rot.

solid	*physical body*		
fluid	*etheric body*	*protein*	*etheric body, abdomen*
gaseous	*astral body*	*fats*	*astral body, chest*
warmth principle	*I*	*starch, sugar*	*I*

Etheric body combats rotting
Astral body combats going rancid
I combats fermentation

I wanted to add to what I said the last time. You know I told you that when someone has taken certain poisons he has to take liquid egg-white protein as an antidote. Things that are healthy become poisons if they are not treated properly in the body, if too much of them gets into the body. Protein can therefore drive away poison in the human being, but protein is itself poisonous if it rots in the body, if too much of it gets into the body. That is how close nutrition and poisoning are to one another. You have no doubt heard that excess food can become poison. A great many diseases are nutritional diseases, that is, people failed to consider that only certain amounts of some substances should be taken if the body is to cope with them.

5. Healthy Nutrition and the Quality of Food

This chapter carries on the theme of the previous one and expands it further to include aspects of how our food is produced and the human being's instinct to eat what he needs—particularly also in children—an instinct that is, however, increasingly being lost.

Today I would like to add a little more in answer to Herr Burle's question of last Thursday. You remember that I spoke of the four substances necessary to human nutrition: minerals, carbohydrates—which are to be found in potatoes, but especially in grains and legumes—then fats and protein. I pointed out how different our nutrition is with regard to protein as compared, for instance, to salt. A person takes salt into his body and it travels all the way to his head, in such a way that the salt remains salt. It is really not changed except that it is dissolved. It keeps its forces as salt all the way through to the human head. In contrast to this, protein—the protein in ordinary hens' eggs, for instance, but also the protein from plants—is at once broken down in the human body, while it is still in the stomach and intestines; it does not remain protein. The human being possesses forces by which he is able to break down this protein. He also has the forces to build something up again, to make his own protein. He would not be able to do this if he had not already broken down other protein.

Now think how it is, gentlemen, with this protein. Imagine that you have become an exceptionally clever person, so clever that you are confident you can make a watch. But you've never seen a watch except from the outside, so you cannot make a watch straight away. But if you take a chance and you take some watch to pieces, take it all apart and lay out the single pieces in such a way that you observe just how the parts relate to one another, then you can see how you are going to put them all together again.

That's what the human body does with protein. It must take in protein and take it all apart.

Protein consists of carbon, nitrogen, oxygen, hydrogen and sulphur. Those are its most important components. And now the protein is completely separated into its parts, so that when it all reaches the intestines we do not have protein in us, but carbon, nitrogen, oxygen, hydrogen and sulphur. You see how it is? Now we have the protein all laid out in its separate parts as the watch was spread out on the table. When I took that watch apart, I observed it very carefully, and now I can make watches. So you may think that I only need to eat protein once; and that after that I can make it myself. But it doesn't happen that way, gentlemen. A human being has his memory as a complete human entity. His body by itself does not have the kind of memory that can take note of something; it uses its 'memory' forces just for building itself up. So one has to continually eat new protein in order to be able to make protein.

The fact is, the human being is involved in a very, very complicated activity when he manufactures his own protein. First he divides the protein he has eaten into its separate parts and disperses the carbon from it everywhere into his body. Now you already know that we inhale oxygen from the air and that this oxygen combines with the carbon we have in us from proteins and other food elements. And we exhale carbon in carbon dioxide, retaining a part of it. So now we have that carbon and oxygen together in our body. We do not retain and use the oxygen that was in the protein; we use the oxygen we have inhaled to combine with the carbon. Thus we do not make our own protein as the materialists describe it, by eating a great many eggs which then are dispersed throughout our body, spread out through our whole body. That is not true.

Actually, we are saved by the organization of our body so that when we eat eggs we don't all turn into crazy hens! It's a fact. We don't become crazy hens because we break the protein down in our intestines, and instead of using the oxygen that was in the protein we use oxygen coming out of the air. Also, as we inhale oxygen we inhale nitrogen too; nitrogen is always in the air. Again, we don't use the nitrogen that comes to us in the hens' eggs; we use the nitrogen we breathe in from the air. And the hydrogen we've eaten in eggs, we don't use that either, not at all. Instead we use the hydrogen we take in through our nose and our ears, through all our senses; that's the hydrogen we use to make our protein. Sulphur too—we receive that continually from the air. Hydrogen and sulphur we get from the air. From the protein we eat, we keep and use only the carbon. The other substances we take from the air. So you see how it is with protein.

There is a similar situation with fat. We make our own protein, using only the carbon from protein we have ingested. And we also make our own fat. For the fats too, we use very little nitrogen from our food. So you see, we produce our own protein and fat. Only what we consume in potatoes, pulses and grains passes into our body. In fact, even these things are not fully absorbed into our body, but only to the lower parts of our head. The minerals we consume go up into the entire head; from them we then obtain what we need to build up our bones.

Therefore you see, gentlemen, we must take care to introduce healthy plant protein into our body. Healthy plant protein! That is what our body needs in large quantities. When we take in protein from eggs, our body can be rather lazy; it can easily break the protein down, because that protein is easily broken down. But plant protein, which we get from fruit—it is chiefly in that part of the plant, as I told you on Thursday—is especially valuable to us. If we want to stay healthy, it is really necessary to include fruit in our diet. Cooked or raw, but fruit we must have. If we neglect to eat fruit, we will gradually condemn our body to a very sluggish digestion.

You can see that it is also a question of giving proper nourishment to the plants themselves. And that means we must realize that plants are living things; they are not minerals, they are something alive. A plant comes to us out of the seed we put in the ground. The plant cannot flourish unless the soil itself is to some degree alive. And how do we make the soil alive? By manuring it properly. Yes, proper manuring is what will give us really good plant protein.

We must remember that for long, long ages people have known that the right manure is what comes out of the horses' stalls, out of the cowshed and so on; the right manure is what comes off the farm itself. In recent times when everything has become materialistic, people have been saying: 'Look, we can do it much more easily by finding out what substances are in the manure and then extracting them from the mineral kingdom—mineral fertilizer!'

And you can see, gentlemen, when one uses artificial mineral fertilizer, it is as if one just put minerals into the ground; then only the root becomes strong. Then we get from the plants the substance that helps to build up our bones. But we don't get a proper protein from the plants. And the plants, our grains, have suffered from lack of protein for a long time. The lack will become greater and greater unless people return to proper manuring.

There have already been agricultural conferences in which the farmers have said: 'Yes, the quality of grain gets worse and worse!' And it is true. But naturally the farmers haven't known the reason. Every older person knows that when he was a young fellow everything that came out of the fields was really better. It's no use thinking that one can make fertilizer simply by combining substances that are present in cow manure. One must see clearly that cow manure does not come out of a chemist's laboratory but out of a laboratory that is far more scientific—it comes from the far, far more scientific laboratory inside the cow. And for this reason cow manure is the stuff that not only makes the roots of plants strong, but also works up powerfully into the crops and produces good, proper protein in the plants which makes us healthy and vigorous.

If there is to be nothing but the mineral fertilizer that has now become so popular, or just manufactured nitrogen, obtained from the air—well, gentlemen, your children, more particularly, your grandchildren will have very pale faces. You will no longer see a difference between their faces and their white hands. Human beings have a lively, healthy colour when farmlands are properly manured.

So you see, when one speaks of nutrition one has to consider how foodstuffs are being cultivated. It is tremendously important. You can see from various circumstances that the human body itself craves what it needs. Here's just one example: people who are in jail for years at a stretch usually get food that contains very little fat, so they develop an enormous craving for fat; and when sometimes a drop of wax falls on the floor from the candle that the guard carries into a cell, the prisoner jumps down at once to lick up the fat. The human body feels the lack so strongly if it is missing some necessary substance. We don't notice this if we eat properly and regularly from day to day; then it never happens that our body is lacking some essential element. But if something is continually lacking in the diet for weeks, then the body becomes exceedingly hungry. That is also something that must be carefully observed.

I have already pointed out that many other things are connected with fertilizing. For instance, our European forefathers in the twelfth and thirteenth centuries, or still earlier, were different from ourselves in many ways. One doesn't usually pay any attention to that fact. Among other things, they had no potatoes! Potatoes were not introduced until later. The potato diet has exercised a strong influence. When grains are eaten, the heart and lungs become particularly strong. Grains strengthen heart and lungs. A person then develops a healthy chest and is in fine health. He is not so keen on thinking as on breathing, perhaps; but he can cope with a good deal when he has good breathing...

And now something more in answer to Herr Burle's question about carrots. Herr Burle said, 'The human body craves instinctively what it needs. Children often pick up a carrot. Children, grown-ups too, are sometimes forced to eat food that is not good for them. I think this is a mistake when someone has a loathing for some food. I have a boy who won't eat potatoes.'

Gentlemen, you need only think of this one thing: if

animals did not have an instinct for what was good for them, and what was bad for them, they would all long since have perished. For animals in a pasture come upon poisonous plants too—all of them—and if they did not know instinctively that they could not eat poisonous plants, they would certainly eat them. But they always pass them by.

But there is something more. Animals choose with care what is good for them. Have you sometimes fattened geese, crammed them with food? Do you think the geese would ever do that themselves? It is only humans who force the geese to eat so much. With pigs it is different; but how thin do you think our pigs might be if we did not encourage them to eat so much? In any case, with pigs it is a little different. They have acquired their characteristics through inheritance; their ancestors had to become accustomed to all the foods that produce fat. These things were acquired through their food in earlier times. But primeval pigs had to be forced to eat so much! No animal ever eats of its own accord what is not right for it.

But now, gentlemen, what has materialism brought about? It no longer believes in such an instinct.

I had a friend in my youth with whom I ate meals very often. We were fairly sensible about our food and would order what we were in the habit of thinking was good for us. Later, as happens in life, we lost track of each other, and after some years I came to the city where he was living and was invited to have dinner with him. And what did I see? Scales beside his plate! I said, 'What are you doing with those scales?' I knew, of course, but I wanted to hear what he would say. He said, 'I weigh the meat they bring me, to eat the right amount—the salad too.' There he was, weighing everything he should put on his plate, because science told him to. And

what had happened to him? He had weaned himself completely from a healthy instinct for what he should eat and
finally no longer knew! And you remember what the textbooks used to say: 'A person needs from 120 to 150 grams of
protein'; he had conscientiously weighed out this precise
amount. Today the proper amount is estimated to be 50
grams, so his amount was incorrect.

Of course, gentlemen, when a person has diabetes, that is
obviously a different situation. The sugar illness, diabetes,
shows that a person has lost his instinct for nutrition.

There you have the gist of the matter. If a child has a
tendency to worms, even the slightest tendency, he will do
everything possible to prevent them. You'll be astonished
sometimes to see such a child hunting for a garden where
there are carrots growing, and then you'll find him there
eating carrots. And if the garden is far off, that doesn't
matter, the child trudges off to it anyway and finds the carrots—because a child who has a tendency to worms longs for
carrots.

And so, gentlemen, the most useful thing you can possibly
do is this. Observe a child when he is weaned, when he no
longer has milk, observe what he begins to like to eat and not
like to eat. The moment a child begins to take external
nourishment, one can learn from him what one should give
him. The moment one begins to urge him to eat what one
thinks he should eat, at that moment his instinct is spoilt.
One should give him the things for which he shows an
instinctive liking. Naturally, if a fondness for something
threatens to go too far, one has to hold it back—but then one
must carefully observe what it is that one is holding back.

For instance, perhaps in your own opinion you are giving a
child every nice thing, and yet the moment that child comes

to the table he cannot help jumping up on his chair and leaning over the table to sneak a lump of sugar! That's something that must be regarded in the right way. For a child who jumps up on his chair to sneak a lump of sugar obviously has something the matter with his liver. Just the simple fact that he must sneak a bit of sugar is a sign that his liver is not in order. Only those children sneak sugar who have something wrong with their livers—it is then actually cured by the sugar. The others are not interested in sugar; they ignore it. Naturally, such a performance can't be allowed to become a habit; but one must have understanding for it. And one can understand it in two ways.

You see, if a child is watching all the time and thinking, 'When will father or mother not be looking, so that I can take that sugar,' then later he will sneak other things. If you satisfy the child, if you give him what he needs, then he doesn't become a thief. It is of great importance from a moral point of view whether one observes such things or not. It is very important, gentlemen.

And so the question that was asked just now must be answered in this way: one should observe carefully what a child likes and what he loathes, and not force him to eat what he does not like. If it happens, for instance, as it does with very many children, that he doesn't want to eat meat, then the fact is that the child gets intestinal toxins from meat and wants to avoid them. His instinct is right. Any child who can sit at a table where everyone else is eating meat and can refuse it certainly has the tendency to develop intestinal toxins from meat. These things must be considered.

You can see that science must become more refined. Science must become much more refined! Today it is far too crude. With those scales, with everything that is carried on in the laboratories, one can't really pursue pure science.

With nutrition, which is the thing particularly interesting us at this moment, one must really acquire a proper understanding of the way it relates to the spirit. I often give two examples. Think, gentlemen, of a journalist, how he has to think so much—and so much of it isn't even necessary. The man must think a great deal, he must think so many logical thoughts; it is almost impossible for any human being to have so many logical thoughts. And so you find that the journalist—or any other person who writes for a profession—loves coffee, quite instinctively. He sits in the coffee shop and drinks one cup after another, and gnaws at his pen so that something will come out that he can write down. Gnawing at his pen doesn't help him, but the coffee does, so that one thought comes out of another, one thought joins onto another.

And then look at diplomats. If one thought joins onto another, if one thought comes out of another, that's bad for them! When diplomats are logical, they're boring. They must be entertaining. In society people don't like to be wearied by logical reasoning—'in the first place—secondly—thirdly'— and if the first and second were not there, the third and fourth would, of course, not have to be thought of! A journalist can't deal with anything but finance in a finance article. But if you're a diplomat you can be talking about night clubs at the same time that you're talking about the economy of country X, then you can comment on the cream-puffs of Lady So-and-So, then you can jump to the rich soil of the colonies, after that discuss where the best horses are being bred, and so on. With a diplomat one thought must leap over into another. So anyone who is obliged to be a charming conversationalist follows his instinct and drinks lots of tea.

Tea scatters thoughts; it lets one leap from one to another. Coffee links one thought to another. If you must leap from one thought to another, then you must drink tea. And one even calls them 'diplomat teas'! Meanwhile the journalist sits in the coffee shop, drinking one cup of coffee after another. You can see what an influence a particular food or drink can have on our whole thinking process. It is so, of course, not just with those two beverages, coffee and tea—those are extreme examples. But precisely from such examples I think you can see that one must consider these things seriously. It is very important, gentlemen.

6. The Processes of Digestion

Rudolf Steiner here takes a closer look at the digestive processes and their effects. Once again, we only see half the story if we look at them purely from a materialistic perspective and ignore the spiritual aspects.

To complete our picture of the human being, let's look more closely at what is going on every day in our body when certain processes take place. After all, we can understand more complex processes only after we have learned about the basic ones. This is why I want to discuss again the processes of nutrition in both their physiological and psychological aspects.

When we eat, we take in food through the mouth. We take in both liquid and solid substances, and by inhaling through the lungs we absorb gaseous ones. But our body can assimilate and use only liquids. Therefore all our solid food must be liquefied already in the mouth. This is accomplished by small glands in our mouth and palate that constantly produce saliva. You must picture them everywhere in the mouth cavity, even along the edge of the tongue. Seen under a microscope the salivary glands resemble small grape bunches because they consist of a cluster of many adjoining cells. They produce saliva, which in turn must dissolve and permeate all food in order to make it digestible.

We perceive this insalivating and permeating activity with our sense of taste. During insalivation we taste the food. Just as we perceive colours with the eyes, so we perceive the flavour of food with the sense of taste.

So, what we eat is insalivated and tasted, savoured, in the mouth. Through our sense of taste we become aware of what we eat. The insalivating process prepares the food for further processing and absorption by the body. But in order to achieve this, the saliva must contain a certain substance called ptyalin, which is produced by the salivary glands and transforms our food so that the stomach can then process it further.

Once our food has been insalivated and permeated with ptyalin, it enters the stomach through the oesophagus. There the food has to be processed further, and for this another special substance is required. This substance is produced in the stomach, just as saliva and the ptyalin it contains are secreted in the mouth. Our stomach, then, produces another kind of saliva that permeates our food. The special substance contained in this saliva is called pepsin.

You see, after the age of seven we no longer have any sense of taste in our stomach. But infants can taste their food there just as adults taste theirs in the mouth. In order to truly understand the human being, we must study the infant's soul life. Adults can at most get an inkling of what it is like to taste in the stomach when this organ is upset and moves the food upwards instead of moving it down into the intestines. Then they get an idea that taste can be perceived in the stomach. I assume that at least some of you have had this experience that food that had already been in the stomach then comes back into the mouth. You will remember that it really tastes much worse than everything we eat, or at least most of it anyway. Foods tasting like what comes back up from the stomach would certainly not be considered a delicacy.

Now this unpleasant taste must have originated somehere. Well, it started in the stomach. In our mouth the food is liquefied and then merely permeated with ptyalin. In the stomach it is further saturated with pepsin, and that is why it now has a different flavour.

There's more to our sense of taste than is immediately apparent. Let's assume you are very sensitive and drink some water. Unless the water has been spoiled, it will not taste bad at all. But if you have eaten a lot of sugar right before that, your tongue is attuned to that flavour, and the water will taste sour. You can see that our sense of taste is quite a complicated thing. However, taste as we adults know it does not originate in the mouth, but in the stomach. Children feel but don't think yet, and that is why they don't know what tasting with the mouth is like. Therefore infants must be given food that does not taste too bad in the stomach. Mother's milk, or also milk in general, is such a food, simply because it does not have a bad flavour in the stomach and because there is a kinship between babies and mother's milk. After all, children are born out of the same body that produces the milk. Because of this relationship between the milk and the baby, the milk does not taste bad in the child's stomach, but if we were to feed infants other food too early they would find those foods repulsive. As adults we don't object to those foods any more because our sense of taste has become coarse. To infants such foods would be repulsive because they have no kinship with them. Thus next to 'stomach' I can write 'child's sense of taste' [see list on page 86].

To return to the food substances in the stomach, once they have been permeated with pepsin they enter the duodenum, the small and the large intestine and so forth. If the chyme simply stayed in the intestines without further processing, it would become hard and destroy us. So something else has to occur, a new activity proceeding from yet another gland. As you know, we have glands in our mouth and in our stomach, and we also have a large one behind the stomach. It is called the pancreas. It secretes a kind of saliva that flows through delicate vessels into the intestines. There the chyme is permeated by this third liquid.

The substance produced by the pancreas is actually transformed in us. At first it closely resembles the pepsin produced in the stomach. On its way towards the intestines, however, it changes. It becomes more strong and pungent, for at this point the chyme must be worked on more strongly than before. This pungent liquid secreted by the pancreas is called trypsin. In other words, the pancreas produces a liquid that becomes trypsin, an acrid substance, in the intestines. It is the third liquid permeating the chyme.

As I said last time, our head-centred consciousness no longer perceives the processes the chyme undergoes. Instead they are perceived, tasted or felt by the liver and thought by the kidneys. The liver and the kidneys have soul qualities and are able to perceive just as we perceive with the sense organs in our head. We are not aware of the liver's and the kidneys' perceptions except, as I said, in dreams; then these perceptions are expressed in a pictorial way. For instance, the chyme advances through the winding intestines and is permeated with trypsin. This acts as a stimulus and can trigger dreams of snakes. At a soul level the perceptions of the liver are thus transformed into something vague and unclear.

So, the liver perceives the processes involving ptyalin, pepsin and trypsin. I'm sorry, but I have to use these dreadful terms scientists unfortunately have coined. Today's so-called experts resent all attempts to clarify things, and they would really be shocked if we gave new names to these substances. We could do this, of course, but I will refrain from shocking scientists unnecessarily with new terms and go on using the old names ptyalin, pepsin and trypsin. The chyme is insalivated three times by three different liquids. These activities are connected to liver perceptions [see list below].

Now, gentlemen, let's try to understand how these liver perceptions take place. As an analogy, think of what happens when you hold a raw onion to your nose. Your eyes water, don't they? If you hold horseradish close to your nose, your eyes fill with tears too. Now why is that? Your eyes water because horseradish and onions work on the tear glands that then excrete bitter tears. The effect of horseradish and onion on the tear glands is roughly like that of the chyme on the liver. The chyme moving through the intestines causes the liver to secrete a kind of tears, namely, bile. The onion must be perceived, must be felt, if it is to cause the production of tears. Similarly, the liver perceives the chyme and adds the bile it has secreted. This then is the fourth liquid our body produces.

Mouth: sense of taste—ptyalin
Stomach: child's sense of taste—pepsin
Pancreas: liver perception—trypsin
Liver: bile

After the chyme has been permeated with ptyalin in the mouth, with pepsin in the stomach, and with trypsin through the pancreas, the liver finally adds bile to it. Only at that point does thinking in the kidneys occur.

After having been permeated by four different liquids, the chyme is absorbed through the intestinal walls into the lymph vessels and then into the blood. You see, then, that very complex life processes take place in the human body. All the way from the mouth to its final absorption by the blood, the chyme is constantly being transformed so that it can be digested properly by the stomach as well as by the entire body.

Now, gentlemen, if we tried to duplicate these processes in a laboratory, even if we were very clever professors, we couldn't do it; we wouldn't be able to duplicate the processes of digestion. We would have to chew the food to permeate it with saliva, then we'd have to saturate it with the liquids produced by stomach, pancreas and liver. Obviously, we wouldn't be able to do all that in a lab; yet these processes are always going on in us, every day of our life. True, we are quite intelligent, but the processes in our belly show much more intelligence than people usually have. The digestive processes are organized very wisely and are not at all easy to duplicate.

You will have even more respect for these processes when I describe them in detail. What do we usually eat? Well, we eat food made from plants, animals and minerals. So there is a wide variety of substances that enter our mouth and then our stomach and intestines, and all of these substances must be transformed through the various processes of insalivation I described.

For instance, think of potatoes. What do they consist of? They consist mainly of starch. When we eat potatoes, we actually eat starch. It is one of our main foods. Potatoes consist almost entirely of starch and of the liquids permeating it, especially water. Because of its contents and the strong life forces in it, the potato looks the way it does. It is actually living starch, which must be destroyed in digestion as I explained. Starch is also contained in other things, not only in potatoes. In fact, all plants contain starch, and we eat starch when we eat plants.

What else do we eat? Whether we eat food from the plant or the animal kingdom, we also take in protein. We also find it in eggs; there it is in its pure form but already somewhat 'deadened'. So we eat protein, as part of meat or plants. We are always eating protein. It is the second most important food.

In addition to starch and protein, we also eat fat. Although there's more fat in animals than in plants, there are certain plant fats. In order to be properly nourished, we need plant or animal fats. They are our third most important food.

Our fourth major food is salt and other minerals. We must either eat foods containing sufficient amounts of salt and minerals or put a salt shaker on the table so that we can add salt to our food because our body needs it.

All of these substances end up in the intestines and are transformed there. Well, and what becomes of them? Because the food substances have been well prepared by saliva and the digestive juices in the stomach, they can be insalivated a third time in the intestines; they won't harden there but will be transformed.

Starch:	sugar
Protein:	liquid protein
Fats:	glycerine, fatty acids
Minerals:	minerals

What becomes of starch in digestion? It is transformed into sugar. In other words, when we eat starch, it becomes sugar in the stomach. If we want to have sugar in us and if we could produce enough of it ourselves, we would not need to eat any for the simple reason that we could manufacture it from starch. But although it is in our nature to be able to do a lot of things, we are not omnipotent. Thus we do not produce enough sugar, in some cases far too little. In order to complement what the intestines themselves normally produce, we must add sugar to our food. To sum up, our intestines transform starch into sugar, which is quite an art.

As you know, people prone to digestive problems find that soft-boiled eggs agree with them better than hard ones. Of course, eggs that have started to rot certainly do not agree with us. Protein is good for us, but if it is still alive when it enters our intestines, it would become unusable and fetid in us, too. We can't use it in our intestines in the form it has outside us. The protein must be transformed first; above all it must be dissolved. It won't dissolve if you merely put it in water. It takes more than just water to dissolve protein. In particular it is trypsin, more than any other liquid, that can liquefy protein.

During this transformation, another substance is formed in our body as a result of the activity of the liquid produced by the pancreas. Strangely enough it is alcohol that develops there. Yes, we produce alcohol in our body. So, we don't really need to drink any alcohol because we are constantly manufacturing it in our intestines. It is only when the liver gets too greedy for alcohol and won't be content with perceiving the small amount of it produced in the intestines that people become alcoholics.

Some people have always known about this and used it to argue in favour of drinking wine and beer. They would argue against teetotallers by saying that we cannot possibly abstain totally from alcohol simply because we all produce some of it in our intestines. Well, this certainly doesn't justify becoming a drinker and demanding an excessive amount of alcohol. If we drink too much alcohol, in other words if we give in to the liver's greed for it, our liver will degenerate into proliferous growth.

After all, the liver has to function properly. If it keeps growing, the small glands in it begin to swell, and then the liver can no longer produce bile of the quality needed. Therefore the chyme is no longer properly permeated with bile and enters lymph and blood vessels without having been properly digested. This imbalance then reaches even the heart and affects it. That is why the liver of people who drink too much beer and so on is ill and looks quite different from that of people who rarely drink or who are content with the small amount of alcohol produced in their own intestines, which should essentially be enough anyway.

Liver and heart disorders result from excessive alcohol consumption. That is why a large number of people in Munich have a so-called beer heart.* Of course, their liver is also damaged for the same reason. You see, we can understand various malfunctions and diseases by examining what happens to the chyme in our organism, by studying the digestive processes.

So when protein is liquefied, alcohol forms and permeates the protein; this prevents the protein from rotting. As you know, if we want to keep something from deteriorating we put it into spirits; for alcohol acts as a preservative. Thus the organism itself can preserve protein by permeating it with the alcohol it has produced. A very wise arrangement, isn't it?

We could not get the same results if we tried to duplicate

---

* Translator's note: The German city of Munich was (and still is) famous for its beer, which is consumed in great quantities by the population, particularly at the world-famous Oktoberfest.

these complicated processes that occur within us. For instance, if we want to preserve a human organ or a small organism, we put it into spirits and display it in a scientific exhibit. But the trypsin fulfils this function in a far more delicate and intelligent way in our intestines. It produces alcohol and uses it to permeate the protein.

And what happens to fats? Well, gentlemen, they enter the intestines and are transformed by both trypsin and bile. Two substances develop out of fats. One of them is glycerine. You already know it in its commercial form; we also produce it in our body. In addition to glycerine, various kinds of fatty acids form when fats are transformed in digestion. Only the salts and minerals undergo little change. They are merely dissolved for easier digestion. They remain basically as they were in the food we ate; they remain unchanged [see list on page 88].

Thus when we eat, we take in starch, protein, fats and minerals. Once we have digested them, they have turned into sugar, dissolved liquefied protein, glycerine, fatty acids, and salt and minerals. What happens then to these transformed substances? Remember, they are now different from the ones we ate. Our organism has changed them.

They say that substances such as sugar, liquefied protein, alcohol, glycerine, fatty acids and minerals all enter the blood vessels, through them get into the heart, and are carried from there to the rest of the organism. Let me say here that all of these substances are of course now liquefied, some are more thickish fluids and others less so, and the thickish liquids do indeed enter the blood vessels and from there reach the rest of the body. However, gentlemen, think of what happens when you put sugar into a glass of water and drink it. Of course, the water isn't sweet only at the bottom, where the sugar settles, but all the water tastes sweet. Sugar dissolves in the water. The same is true for salt. This glass of water, which we might compare with the human body, does not need special vessels to distribute the sugar or salt everywhere, because they are absorbed everywhere by the liquid.

I told you some time ago that human beings consist of 90 per cent water, or at least liquids. We are talking of living water here, but water nonetheless. Now, do these transformed substances then really need blood vessels in order to be absorbed by the entire body? Does the sugar produced in our intestines need special vessels to reach all parts of our organism? No, of course not. We human beings consist of so much water for the very purpose of distributing the sugar everywhere.

People used to say that the alcohol a drinker consumes enters the heart by way of the intestines and from there is then distributed throughout the body. Let me assure you, gentlemen, if all this alcohol entered the heart first, the person would not die in a few years, but in a few days instead. In fact, it can be proved that any liquid food we take in doesn't reach the rest of the body by way of the blood vessels, but instead in the same way sugar added to a glass of water is distributed in all of the water.

True, when a healthy person is thirsty and drinks a glass of water, then this water is assimilated and added to the chyme in the intestines as needed and reaches the heart and the rest of the body by way of the blood vessels. However, once the blood vessels and the heart have received enough, no more water is distributed through the vessels, no matter how much we drink. No more water is needed there. If we drink just enough to quench our thirst—say one glass or one and a half—it doesn't do any harm at all. But anything beyond that amount, any excess—say, a third or fourth glass—will lead to excretion of the water in urine. This unnecessary liquid will not, as it were, bother to go through the heart, but since our organism is a column of water and this extra amount is superfluous, it is simply discharged with the urine. Just imagine what happens when people sit in a pub or a bar and have their third or fourth glass of beer. You can see them get up and walk away somewhere! This beer did not take the time to go through the heart first; it left by a shortcut, because, after all, the human organism is essentially liquid.

Thus, we can summarize as follows. The chyme, consisting of sugar, liquid protein, glycerine, fatty acids and minerals, is absorbed directly by the entire organism. Only the more thickish liquids are distributed by means of the blood vessels. That's why minerals can be deposited in our head and other organs; they get there not through the blood vessels, but enter the organs directly.

If we'd always feel the salt and minerals being deposited in our heads, we would suffer from headaches. An excess of salt in the head causes pain there. You've probably heard of migraine, which we've already discussed earlier. Things can be explained on different levels. What is migraine? It is brought about by excessive mineral deposits, particularly of uric acid, in the head. The uric acid is not excreted with the urine, but remains in the head. This is because food was not prepared properly and retained minerals. Migraine is not such a 'refined' illness, after all, even though it mainly afflicts 'refined' people. Migraine is actually a rather indecent illness. Substances that should have been excreted with the urine remain instead in the right part of the head because they were already beginning to deteriorate in the stomach. In other words, whatever works on the left side of the organism affects the right side of the head. I'll explain in a minute why this is so.

How much salt and mineral substances can our organism put up with? Remember, as I said earlier, our head contains brain fluid. It is only because of this brain fluid that our brain is light enough for our organism. As you know, a solid object has a certain heaviness or weight in air, but when we put it into water, its weight is reduced. If this were not so, we would not be able to swim. If the brain were not suspended in fluid, its weight would be about three pounds or 1500 grams. Suspension in brain fluid reduces the weight of the brain to a mere ounce or about 20 grams.

However, accumulating salt deposits increase the weight again and make the brain too heavy. True, being suspended in fluid decreases the weight of the brain as well as that of the salts deposited there. But now think of the differences between human beings and animals. You see, our head is put on top of the rest of the organism, which thus supports the brain. This is different in animals; there the head lacks this solid support and hangs, as it were, over the front of the body. What are the consequences of this difference? In human beings the slight pressure of the head is absorbed by the body. This pressure is not absorbed in this way in animals, and this is a major difference between humans and animals.

Scientists are always trying to figure out how humans evolved from animals. Well, it's all right to try to understand this, but, really, that's not the way to look at human beings. For example, we can't say that because monkeys have so and so many bones and human beings have the same number they are basically alike. It doesn't change the fact that even in gorillas or orang-utans the head hangs down over the front of the body, no matter how upright they walk. The human head, on the other hand, is supported by the upright body that absorbs the pressure.

Something very remarkable is going on in us there. The minerals we have in us move from the stomach to the head and are deposited there. If there's too much of them, they have to return through the body to be excreted. But something else must also happen to the other substances we have in us after digestion. While they move upwards, they undergo another transformation because the upright body partly offsets gravity. These substances in part become lighter, and in part they become more concentrated, condensed, and then form sediments. As we often find sediments when we try to dissolve something, so here there are sediments or deposits along the way as these substances move from the stomach to the head. Well, the smallest particles move upwards, and on the way they are transformed by the reduced gravity. What happens to them now? These substances originating in our food now turn into a kind of phosphorus. Indeed, the nutrient substances are not merely moving up into the head, but on the way some of the sugar, glycerine, and so forth is transformed into phosphorus.

You see, there are basically two kinds of substances in our head: salt and other minerals, which are still pretty much as they were before we ingested them with our food, and phosphorus, diffused like air, in fact in a dispersion even finer than that of air. These two, salts and phosphorus, are what we mainly find in our head. The others are present merely to keep us alive. But the two most important substances in the human head are salts and phosphorus.

As I'll show you later, it is possible to prove that human beings cannot think properly if they don't get the salt and other minerals they need. We need salts and minerals for our thinking. Adding this point to what we have already said about thinking, you can see that human beings are very complicated.

$$\text{Head} \begin{cases} \text{salt: thinking} \\ \text{phosphorus: willing} \end{cases}$$

If we have too much phosphorus in us, which is due to eating food that's too spicy, then we get fidgety like a spoiled child, wanting to touch and have everything. Phosphorus is responsible for our willing. If there's too much phosphorus, our will becomes fidgety. When this excessive phosphorus level reaches our head, we will not only be fidgety and nervous (which is due to the phosphorus, not to the nerves), but we will actually throw fits and go raving mad. In order to be able to have any will at all, we must have a small amount of phosphorus. But too much of it makes us insane.

Well, imagine someone gives you some salt, and you want to get it to think. How would you do that? But you are actually doing this very thing all the time. In our head we always use salt to think. Next, scrape a bit of fine, powdery phosphorus off the tip of a match and try to set it on fire. This substance is supposed to have will, to be full of will-power. Oh, it'll burn and evaporate all right, but it won't develop any will-power. Yet we are doing this very thing all the time inside our body.

Don't you see now that there's something in you that is more intelligent than your poor head, which cannot transform salt into a being of rational thought nor phosphorus into a being of will? This something in us is what we can call the soul-spirit, living and working in us. It uses the salt and minerals in the head for thinking and takes the phosphorus, finely dispersed like smoke, for willing.

If we study things in the right way, we move from the physical to the soul-spiritual realm. But modern scientists don't look beyond the stomach. At most, they know that sugar and other substances develop in the stomach. Then they lose track of how substances are distributed in the body and ignore what happens beyond this point. This is why conventional science doesn't have anything to say about soul-spiritual matters. This limited science must be extended and supplemented. We must not restrict ourselves to the stomach and think of the head as merely tagged on at the top of the body. How salts and phosphorus get up into the head can't be seen. People therefore imagine that the same processes as in the stomach also take place in the head. This is because modern scientists usually know only something about the stomach; yet even there they merely realize that new substances are formed but do not know that the liver perceives and the kidneys think. They don't know this because, after all, they don't know very much about the head either.

That's why conventional science does not even look for anything else, thinking the liver on the autopsy table provides complete information. But the information to be gained from this liver is far from complete, because at the time when it was removed from the body the liver had already lost its soul forces. As long as soul forces are in the organs, the latter can't be removed from the body.

There you can see that a truly serious science has to continue where our modern science stops. That's what's important. That's why we have built the Goetheanum here, to enable scientists to know not just something incomplete about the stomach, but instead to be able to explain the entire body. When they can do that, they will represent true science.

7. The Effect of Plant, Raw Food, Vegetarian and Meat Diets

Plants and vegetables form a key part of the human diet, indeed, of human existence through photosynthesis. The importance of plants is a recurring theme in Rudolf Steiner's reflections on nutrition and is emphasized here once again, this time particularly from the perspective of the carbon cycle as it involves plants and human beings. This leads on to a discussion of the merits or otherwise of eating only raw vegetables, and vegetarian and meat diets. This is also where Steiner warns of feeding bovines with meat products against their natural herbivorous diet, anticipating 'mad-cow disease' and the BSE crisis.

Rudolf Steiner: Good morning, gentlemen! Has someone thought of a question during the last weeks?

Question: I would like to ask about various foods—beans and carrots, for instance. What effect do they have on the body? You have already spoken about potatoes; perhaps we could hear something about other foodstuffs. Some vegetarians won't eat things that hang down, like beans or peas. And when one looks at a field of grain, one wonders how the various grains differ—for apparently all the peoples of the earth cultivate some grain or other.

Rudolf Steiner: So, the question is about the relation of various foods to the human body. Well, first of all we should gain a clear idea of nutrition itself. One's immediate thought of nutrition is that when we eat something, it goes through the mouth down into the stomach, then it is deposited in the body and finally we get rid of it; then we must eat again, and so on. But the process is not as simple as that. It is much more complicated. And if one wants to understand how the human being is really related to various foods, one must first be clear about the kinds of food one definitely needs.

Now the very first thing one needs, the substance one must have without fail, is protein. Let us write all this on the board, so that we have a complete overview. So, protein, as it is in a hen's egg, for instance—but not just in eggs; protein is in all foods. One definitely needs protein. The second thing one needs is fats. These too are in all foods. Plants contain fats too. The third thing has a name that will be less familiar to you, but one needs to know it: carbohydrates.

Carbohydrates are found particularly in potatoes, but they are also found in large quantity in all other plants. The important fact about carbohydrates is that when we eat them they are slowly turned into starch by the saliva in our mouth and the secretions in our stomach. Starch is something we need without fail, but we don't eat starch; we eat foods that contain carbohydrates, and the carbohydrates are turned into starch inside us. Then they are converted once again, in the further process of digestion, into sugar. And we need sugar. So you see, we get the sugar we need from the carbohydrates. But we still need something else: minerals. We get them partly by adding them to our food, for example in the form of salt, and partly they are already contained in all our food.

Now when we consider protein, we must realize how greatly it differs in animals and human beings from what it is in plants. Plants contain protein too, but they don't eat it, so where do they get it from? They get it out of the ground and out of the air, from the mineral world; they can take their protein from lifeless, mineral sources. Neither animal nor the human being can do that. A human being cannot use the protein that is to be got from lifeless elements—he would then only be a plant. He must get his protein as it is already available in plants or animals.

Actually, to be able to live on this earth the human being needs the plants. But now this is the amazing fact: the plants could not live on the earth either if human beings were not here! So, gentlemen, we reach the interesting fact—and we must grasp it quite clearly—that of all things the two most essential for human life are the green sap in the green leaves and blood. The green in the sap of a plant is called chlorophyll. Chlorophyll is contained in the green leaf. And the other essential thing is blood.

Now this brings us to something very remarkable. Think how you breathe—that is also a way of taking in nourishment. You take oxygen in from the air; you breathe it in. But there is carbon spread through your entire body. If you go down into the earth where there are coal deposits, you find black coal. When you sharpen a pencil, you've got graphite. Coal and graphite—they're both carbon. Your whole body is made of carbon (as well as other substances). Carbon is formed in the human body. You could say a person is just a heap of black coal! But you could also say something else. Remember the most expensive thing in the world? A diamond—and that's made of carbon; it just has a different form. And so, if you like the sound of it better, you could say you're made of glittering diamonds. The black carbon, that graphite in the pencil, and the diamonds: they are all the same substance. If someday the coal that is dug out of the earth can by some process be made transparent, you'll have diamonds. So we have diamonds hidden in our body. Or we are a coal field!

But now when oxygen combines with carbon in the blood, you have carbon dioxide. And you know carbon dioxide quite well, you only have to think of Seltzer water with the bubbles in it: they are the carbon dioxide. It is a gas. So one can have this picture: a human being inhales oxygen from the air, the oxygen spreads all through his blood; in his blood he has carbon, and he exhales carbon dioxide. You breathe oxygen in, you breathe carbon dioxide out.

In the course of the earth's evolution, gentlemen, which I have recently been describing to you, everything would long ago have been poisoned by the carbon dioxide coming from human beings and animals. For this evolution has been going on a long time. As you can see, there could have been no human kingdom or animal kingdom alive on the earth for a long, long time now unless plants had had a very different character from people and animals. Plants do not take in oxygen; they take in the carbon dioxide that human beings and animals exhale. Plants are just as greedy for carbon dioxide as human beings are for oxygen.

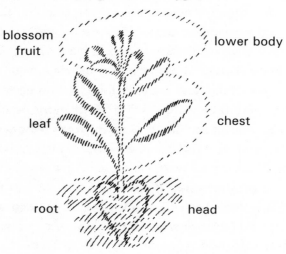

Now if we look at a plant [see drawing]—root, stem, leaves, blossoms—the plant absorbs carbon dioxide into every part of it. And now the carbon in the carbon dioxide is deposited in the plant, and the oxygen is breathed out by the plant. Human beings and animals get it back again. The human being gives carbon dioxide out and kills everything; the plant keeps back the carbon, releases the oxygen and brings everything to life again. And the plant could do nothing with the carbon dioxide if it did not have its green sap, the chlorophyll. This green sap of the plant, gentlemen, is a magician. It retains carbon inside the plant and lets the oxygen go free. Our blood combines oxygen with carbon; the green plant-sap separates the carbon again from the carbon dioxide and sets the oxygen free. Think what an excellent arrangement nature has made, that plants and animals and human beings should complement one another in this way! They complement one another perfectly.

But that is not all. The human being not only needs the oxygen that the plant gives him, he needs the entire plant.

With the exception of poisonous plants and certain plants which contain very little of these substances, the human being needs all plants not only for his breathing but also for food. And that brings us to another remarkable connection. A plant consists of root, if it is an annual plant (we won't consider the trees at this moment)—of root, leaf and stem, blossom and fruit. Now look at the root for a moment. It is in the earth. It contains many minerals, because minerals are in the earth and the root clings to the earth with its tiny fine rootlets, so it is constantly absorbing those minerals. So the root of the plant has a special relation to the mineral realm of the earth.

And now look here, gentlemen! The part of the human being that is related to the whole earth is the head. Not the feet, but actually the head. When the human being starts to be an earthly being in the womb, he has at first almost nothing but a head. He begins with his head. His head takes the shape of the whole cosmos and the shape of the earth. And the head particularly needs minerals. For it is from the head that the forces go out that fill the human body with bones, for instance. Everything that makes a human being solid is the result of the way the head has been formed. While the head itself is still soft, as in the womb, it cannot form bones properly. But as it becomes harder and harder itself, it passes to the body the forces by which both the human being and animal are able to form their solid parts, particularly their bones. You can see from this that we need roots. They are related to the earth and contain minerals. We need the minerals for bone-building. Bones consist of calcium carbonate, calcium phosphate; those are minerals. So you can see that the human being needs roots in order to strengthen his head.

And so, gentlemen, if for instance a child is becoming weak in his head—inattentive, hyperactive—he will usually have a corresponding symptom: worms in his intestines.

Worms develop easily in the intestines if the head forces are too weak, because the head does not then work down strongly enough into the rest of the body. Worms find no lodging in a human body if the head forces are working down strongly into the intestines. You can see how magnificently the human body is arranged!—everything is related. And if one's child has worms, one should realize the child's head-forces are weakened. Also—anyone who wants to be a teacher has to know these things—if there are persons who at a later age are weak-minded, one can be sure they had worms when they were young.

And so what must one do if one observes this in the child? The simplest remedy is to give him carrots to eat for a while—with his other food, of course; naturally, one couldn't just feed him on carrots alone. Carrots are the root of the plant. They grow down in the earth and have a large quantity of minerals. They have the forces of the earth in them, and when they are taken into the stomach they are able to work up through the blood into the head. Only substances rich in minerals are able to reach the head. Substances rich in minerals, root substances, give strength to a human being by way of the head. That is extraordinarily important. It is through carrots that the uppermost parts of the head become strong—which is precisely what the human being needs in order to be inwardly firm and vigorous, not soft.

If you look at the carrot plant, you can't help seeing that its strength has gone particularly into the root. It is almost entirely root. The only part of the plant one is interested in is the root. The rest of it, the green part, is of no importance, it just sits there up above. So the carrot is particularly good as a food substance to maintain the human head. And if sometimes you yourselves feel empty-headed, dull, can't think properly, then it's fine if you too eat carrots for a while! Naturally, they will help children the most.

But now if we compare a potato to a carrot—well, first of all it looks quite different. Of course, the potato plant has a green part. And then it has the part we eat, what we call the tubers, deep down in the earth. Now if we would think superficially, we could say those tubers are the roots. But that is not correct; the tubers are not roots. If you look carefully down into the soil, you can see the real roots hanging on the tubers. The real roots are tiny rootlets, root hairs, that hang on the tubers. They fall away easily. When you gather up the potatoes, the hairs have already fallen away. Only in the first moment when you are lifting a potato loose from the soil the hairs are still all over it. When we eat a potato, we are really eating a piece of swollen, enlarged stem. It only appears to be a root; in reality it is stem or metamorphosed foliage. The potato is something down there between the root and the stem. Therefore it does not have as much mineral content as the carrot; it is not as earthy. It grows in the earth, but it is not so strongly related to the earth. And it contains particularly carbohydrates; not so many minerals, but carbohydrates.

So now, gentlemen, you can say to yourselves: 'When I eat carrots, my body can really take it easy, for all it needs is saliva to soften the carrot.' All it needs is saliva and stomach secretions, pepsin and so forth for all the important substance of the carrot to reach the head. We need minerals, and minerals are furnished by any kind of root, but in greatest amounts by such a root as the carrot.

But now, when we eat potatoes, first they go into the mouth and stomach. There the body has to exert strength to derive starch from them. Then the digestive process goes further in the intestines. In order that something can go into the blood and also reach the head, there must be more exertion still, because sugar has to be derived from the starch. Only then can it go to the head. So one has to use still greater forces. Now think of this, gentlemen: when I exert my strength upon some external thing, I become weak. This is really a secret of human physiology: that if I chop wood, if I use my external bodily strength, I become weak; but if I exert an inner strength, transforming carbohydrates into starch and starch into sugar, I become strong. Precisely through the fact that I permeate myself with sugar by eating potatoes, I become strong. When I use my strength externally, I become weak; if I use it internally, I become strong. So it is not a matter of simply filling oneself up with food, but of the food generating strength in our body.

And so one can say: food from roots—and all roots have the same effect as carrots although not to the same degree, they all work particularly on the head—food from roots gives the body what it needs for itself. Foods that lean towards the green of the plant and contain carbohydrates provide the body with strength it needs for work, for movement.

I have already spoken about the potato. While it requires a terribly large expenditure of strength, it leaves a person weak afterwards, and does not provide him with any continuing strength. But the principle I have just given you holds good even for the potato.

Now to the same extent that the potato is a rather poor foodstuff, all the grains—wheat, rye, and so on—are good foodstuffs. The grains also contain carbohydrates, and of such a nature that the human being forms starch and sugar in the healthiest possible way. Actually, the carbohydrates of the grains can make him stronger than he can make himself by any other means. Only think for a moment how strong people are who live on farms, simply through the fact that they eat large quantities of their own home-made bread which contains the grain from their fields! They only need to have healthy bodies to start with, then if they can digest the rather coarse bread it is really the healthiest food for them. They must first have healthy bodies, but then they become quite especially strong through the process of making starch and sugar.

Now a question might be raised. You see, human beings have come in the course of their evolution, quite of their own accord one can say, to eat the grains differently from the way animals eat them. A horse eats his oats almost as they grow. Animals eat their kernels of grain raw, just as they come from the plant. The birds would have a hard time getting their seed if they had to depend upon someone cooking it for them first! But human beings have come of themselves to cook the grains. And now, gentlemen, what happens when we cook the grain? Well, when we cook the grain, we don't eat it cold, we eat it warm. And it's a fact, that to digest our food we need inner warmth. Unless there is warmth we can't transform our carbohydrates into starch and the starch into sugar—that requires inner heat.

So if we first apply external heat to the foodstuffs, we help the body so that it does not have to provide all the warmth itself. By being cooked first, the foods have already begun the fire process, the warmth process. That's the first result. The second is that they have been entirely changed. Think what happens to the grain when I make flour into bread. It becomes something quite different. And how has it become different? Well, first I have ground the seeds. What does that mean? I have crushed them into tiny, tiny pieces. And you see, what I do there with the seeds, grinding them, making them fine, I'd otherwise have to do later within my own body! Everything I do externally I'd otherwise have to do internally, inside my body; so by doing those things I relieve my body. And the same with the baking itself: all the things I do through cooking I save my body from doing. I bring the foods to a condition in which my body can more easily digest them.

You have only to think of the difference if someone would eat raw potatoes instead of cooked ones. If someone were to eat his potatoes raw, his stomach would have to provide a tremendous amount of warmth to transform those raw potatoes—which are almost starch already. And the extent to which it could transform them would not be sufficient. So then the potatoes would reach the intestines and the intestines would also have to use a great amount of energy. Then the potatoes would just stay put in the intestines, for the subsequent forces would not be able to carry them farther into the body. So if one eats raw potatoes, either one just loads one's stomach with them and the intestines can't even get started on them or one fills up the intestines; in either case there is no further digestion. But if the potatoes undergo a preparatory stage through cooking or some other means, then the stomach does not have so much to do, or the intestines either, and the potatoes enter the blood properly and continue into the head. So, you see, by cooking our foods, especially those that are counted among the carbohydrates, we are able to help our nutrition.

You are certainly acquainted with all the new kinds of foolishness in connection with nutrition—for instance, the raw food faddists, who are not going to cook anything any more, they're going to eat everything raw. How does this come about? It's because people no longer gain the knowledge they need from a materialistic science, and they shy away from a spiritual science, so they think a few things out on their own. The whole raw food fad is a fantasy. For a time someone living on raw food can whip the body along—in this situation the body has to draw on very strong forces, so you can say it needs to be whipped—but then it will collapse all the more completely.

But now, gentlemen, let us come to the fats. Plants, almost all of them, contain fats which they derive from the minerals. Now fats do not enter the human body so easily as carbohydrates and minerals. Minerals are not really changed at all. For example, when you shake salt into your soup, that salt goes almost unchanged up into your head. You get it as salt in your head. But when you eat potatoes, you don't get potatoes in your head, you get sugar. The conversion takes place as I described to you. With the fats, however, whether they're plant fats or animal fats, it's not such a simple matter. When fats are eaten, they are almost entirely eaten up by the saliva, by the gastric secretions, by the intestinal secretions, and they become something quite different that then passes into the blood. The animal and the human being must form their own fats in their intestines and in their blood, with forces which the fats they eat call forth.

You see, that is the difference between fats and sugar or minerals. The human being still takes his salt and his sugar from nature. He has to derive the sugar from the potato and the rye and so on, but there is still something of nature in it. But with the fats that the human being or animal have in them, there is nothing of nature left. They form them themselves. The human being would have no strength if he did not eat; his intestines and blood need fats. So we can say that the human being himself cannot form minerals. If he did not take in minerals, his body would never be able to build them by itself. If he did not take in carbohydrates, if he did not eat bread or something similar from which he gets carbohydrates, he would never be able to form sugar by himself. And if he could not form sugar, he would be a weakling forever. So be grateful for the sugar, gentlemen! Because you are chock-full of sweetness, you have strength. The moment you were no longer full to the brim with your own sweetness, you would have no strength, you would collapse.

And you know, that is even true of the various nationalities and peoples. There are certain peoples who consume very little sugar or foods that produce sugar. These peoples have weak physical forces. Then there are certain peoples who eat many carbohydrates that form sugar, and they are strong.

But human beings don't have such an easy time with fats. If someone has fats in him (and this is true also of the animals), that is his own accomplishment, the accomplishment of his body. Fats are entirely his own production. The human being destroys whatever fats he takes in, plant fats or animal fats, and through their destruction he develops strength. With potatoes, rye, wheat, he develops strength by converting the substances. With the fats that he eats he develops strength by destroying their substances.

If I destroy something outside of myself, I become tired and exhausted. And if I have had a big fat beefsteak and destroy that inside myself, I become weak in the same way; but my destruction of the fat beefsteak or of the plant fat gives me strength again, so that I can produce my own fat if my body is predisposed to it. So you see, the consumption of fat works very differently in the human body from the consumption of carbohydrates. The human body, gentlemen, is exceedingly complicated, and what I have been describing to you is tremendous work. Much must take place in the human body for it to be able to destroy those plant fats.

But now let us think how it is when someone eats green stuff, the stems and leaves of a plant. When he eats green stuff, he is getting fats from the plants. Why is it that sometimes a stem is so hard? Because it gives its forces to leaves that are going to be rich in carbohydrates. And if the leaves stay green—the greener they are, the more fats they have in them. So when someone eats bread, for instance, he can't absorb many fats from the bread. He takes in more, for example, from watercress—that tiny plant with very tiny leaves—more fats than when he eats bread. That's how the custom came about of putting butter on our bread, some kind of fat. It wasn't just for the taste. And why country people want bacon with their bread. There again is fat, and that also is eaten for two reasons.

When I eat bread, the bread works upon my head because the root elements of a plant work up into the stem. The stem, even though it is stem and grows above the ground in the air, still has root forces in it. The question is not whether something is above in the air, but whether it has any root forces. Now the leaf, the green leaf, does not have root forces. No green leaf ever unfolds down in the earth. In late summer and autumn, when sun forces are no longer working so strongly, the stem can mature. But the leaf needs the strongest sun forces for it to unfold; it grows towards the sun. So we can say that the green part of the plant works particularly on heart and lungs, while the root strengthens the head. The potato is also able to work into the head. When we eat greens, they chiefly give us plant fats; they strengthen our heart and lungs, the middle region, the chest.

That, I would say, is the secret of human nutrition—that if I want to work upon my head, I have roots or stems for dinner. If I want to work upon my heart or my lungs, I make myself a green salad. And in this case, because these substances are destroyed in the intestines and only their forces work on in us, cooking is not so necessary. That's why leaves can be eaten raw as salad. Whatever is to work on the head cannot be eaten raw; it must be cooked. Cooked foods work particularly on the head. Lettuce and similar things work particularly on heart and lungs, building them up, nourishing them through the fats.

But now, gentlemen, the human being must not only nurture the head and the middle body, the chest region, but he must nurture the digestive organs themselves. He needs a stomach, intestines, kidneys and a liver, and he must build up these digestive organs himself. Now the interesting fact is this: to build up his digestive organs he needs protein for food, the protein that is in plants, particularly as contained in their blossoms, and most particularly in their fruit. So we can say: the root nourishes the head particularly [see drawing page 102]; the middle of the plant, stem and leaves, nourishes the chest particularly; and fruit nourishes the abdomen.

When we look out at our grain fields we can say, good that they are there for that nourishes our head. When we look down at the lettuce we've planted, all those leaves that we eat without cooking because they are easily digested in the intestines—and it's their forces that we want—there we get everything that maintains our chest organs. But cast an eye up at the plums and apples, at the fruits growing on the trees. Ah! those we don't have to bother to cook much, for they've been cooked by the sun itself during the whole summer! There an inner ripening has already been happening, so that they are something quite different from the roots, or from stalks and stems (which are not ripened but actually dried up by the sun). The fruits, as I said, we don't have to cook much—unless we have a weak organism, in which case the intestines cannot destroy the fruits. Then we must cook them; we must have stewed fruit and the like. If someone has intestinal illnesses, he must be careful to take his fruit in some cooked form—sauce, jam, and so forth. If one has a perfectly healthy digestive system, a perfectly healthy intestinal system, then fruits are the right thing to nourish the abdomen, through the protein they contain. Protein from any of the fruits nourishes your stomach for you, nourishes all your digestive organs in your abdomen.

You can see what a good instinct human beings have had for these things! Naturally, they have not known in concepts all that I've been telling you, but they have known it instinctively. They have always prepared a mixed diet of roots, greens and fruit; they have eaten all of them, and even the comparative amounts that one should have of these three different foods have been properly determined by their instinct.

But now, as you know, people not only eat plants, they eat animals too, the flesh of animals, animal fat and so on.

Certainly it is not for anthroposophy ever to assume a fanatical or a sectarian attitude. Its task is only to tell how things are. One simply cannot say that people should eat only plants, or that they should also eat animals, and so on. One can only say that some people with the forces they have from heredity are simply not strong enough to perform within their bodies all the work necessary to destroy plant fats, to destroy them so completely that then forces will develop in their bodies for producing their own fat. You see, a person who eats only plant fats—well, either he's renounced the idea of becoming an imposing, portly fellow or else he must have an awfully good digestive system, so healthy that it is easy for him to break down the plant fats and in this way get forces to build his own fat. Most people are really unable to produce their own fat if they have only plant fats to destroy. When one eats animal fat in meat, that is not entirely broken down. Plant fats don't go out beyond the intestines, they are broken down in the intestines. But the fat contained in meat does go beyond; it passes right into the human being. And then it is fine for a person to be weaker than if he were on a diet of just plant fats.

Therefore, we must distinguish between two kinds of

bodies. First there are the bodies that do not like fat, they don't enjoy eating bacon, they just don't like to eat fatty foods. Those are bodies that destroy plant fats comparatively easily and want to form their own fat. They say: 'Whatever fat I carry around, I want to make myself; I want my very own fat.' But if someone heaps his table with fatty foods, then he's not saying, 'I want to make my own fat.' He's saying, 'The world must give me my bacon.' For animal fat passes into the body, making the work of nutrition easier.

When a child sucks a sweet, he's not doing that for nourishment. There is, to be sure, something nutritious in it, but the child doesn't suck it for that; he sucks it for the sweet taste. The sweetness is the object of his consciousness. But if an adult eats beef fat, or pork fat, or the like, well, that passes into his body. It satisfies his craving just as the sweet satisfies the child's craving. But it is not quite the same, for the adult feels this craving deeper inside him. The adult needs this inner craving in order to respond to his inner being. That is why he loves meat. He eats it because his body loves it.

But it is no use being fanatical about these things. There are people who simply cannot live if they don't have meat. A person must consider carefully whether he really will be able to get on without it. If he does decide he can do without it and changes over from a meat to a vegetarian diet, he will feel stronger than he was before. That's sometimes a difficulty, obviously; some people can't bear the thought of living without meat. If, however, someone does become a vegetarian, he feels stronger because he is no longer obliged to deposit alien fat in his body; he makes his own fat, and this makes him feel stronger.

I know this from my own experience. I could not otherwise have endured the strenuous exertion of these last 24 years! I never could have travelled entire nights, for instance, and then given a lecture the next morning. For it is a fact that if one is a vegetarian one carries out a certain activity within one that is spared the non-vegetarian, who has it done first by an animal. That's the important difference.

But now don't get the idea that I'm making propaganda on behalf of vegetarianism! It must always be first established whether a person is able to become a vegetarian or not; it is an individual matter.

You see, this is especially important in connection with protein. One can digest protein if one is able to eat plant protein and break it down in the intestines. And then one gets the forces from it. But the moment the intestines are weak, one must get the protein externally, which means one must eat the right kind of protein, which will be animal protein. Hens that lay eggs are also animals! So protein is something that is really judged quite falsely unless it is considered from an anthroposophical point of view.

When I eat roots, their minerals go up into my head. When I eat salad greens, their forces go to my chest, lungs and heart—not their fats, but the forces from their fats. When I eat fruit, the protein from the fruit stays in the intestines. And the protein from animal substances goes beyond the intestines into the body; animal protein spreads out. One might think, therefore, that if a person eats plenty of protein he will be a well-nourished individual. This has led to the fact in this materialistic age that people who had studied medicine were recommending excessive amounts of protein for the average diet. They maintained that 120–150 grams of protein were necessary—which was ridiculous. Today it is known that only a quarter of that amount is necessary. And actually, if a person does eat such enormous and unnecessary amounts of protein—well, then something happens as it once did with a certain professor and his assistant.

They had a person suffering from malnutrition and they wanted to build him up with protein. Now it is generally recognized that when someone is consuming large amounts of protein—it is, of course, converted in him—his urine will show that he has had it in his diet. So now it happened in this case that the person's urine showed no sign of the protein being present in his body. It didn't occur to them that it had already passed through the intestines. The professor was in a terrible state. And the assistant was shaking in his boots as he said timidly: 'Sir ... Professor ... perhaps ... through the intestines?' Of course!

What had happened? They had stuffed the person with protein and it was of no use to him, for it had gone from the stomach into the intestines and then out behind. It had not spread into the body at all. If one gulps down too much protein, it doesn't pass into the body at all, but into the faecal waste matter. Even so, the body does get something from it; before it passes out, it lies there in the intestines and becomes poisonous and poisons the whole body. That's what can happen from too much protein. And from this poisoning arteriosclerosis often results so that many people get arteriosclerosis too early, simply from stuffing themselves with too much protein.

It is important, as I have tried to show you, to know these things about nutrition. For most people are thoroughly convinced that the more they eat the better they are nourished. Of course it is not true. One is often much better nourished if one eats less, because then one does not poison oneself.

The point is really that one must know how the various

substances work. One must know that minerals work particularly on the head. Carbohydrates—just as they are to be found in our most common foods, bread and potatoes, for instance—work more on the lung system and throat system (lungs, throat, palate, and so on). Fats work particularly on heart and blood vessels, arteries and veins, and protein particularly on the abdominal organs. The head has no special amount of protein. What protein it does have—naturally, it also has to be nourished with protein, for after all, it consists of living substances—is protein we have to form ourselves. And if one overeats, it's no use believing that by this means one is getting a healthy brain, for just the opposite is happening: one is getting a poisoned brain.

Protein:	abdominal organs
Fats:	heart and blood vessels
Carbohydrates:	lungs, throat, palate
Minerals:	head

Now, the human being constantly eats. He eats animal substances and he eats those of plants. I have told you before that I have no intention of promoting one or another form of diet. I only point out the effects. Vegetarians have frequently come to me saying they are prone to slight fainting spells, and so on. I have told them that it is because they don't eat meat. These matters must be viewed quite objectively; one must not desire to force something. What is the 'objective view', however, regarding eating plants and eating meat? Consider the plant. A plant manages to develop the seed that is planted in the earth all the way to green leaves and colourful flower petals. Now, you either receive your nourishment directly from grains or you pluck a cabbage and make soup or something. Compare what you get from the plant with what is present in meat, usually an animal's muscle. Meat is a completely different substance from the plant. What is the relationship between these two substances?

You know that there are some animals that are simply gentle vegetarian beings. There are animals that do not eat meat. Cows, for example, eat no meat. Neither are horses keen on meat; they also eat only plants. Now, you must be clear that an animal not only absorbs food but is also constantly shedding what is inside its body. Among birds you know that there is something called moulting. The birds lose their feathers and must replace them with new ones. You know that deer drop their antlers. You cut your nails, and they grow back. What appears outwardly so visible here is part of a continuous process. We constantly shed our skins. I have explained this to you once before. During a period of approximately seven to eight years, our entire bodies are shed and replaced with new ones. This is also the case with animals.

Consider a cow or an ox. After some years the flesh within it has been entirely replaced. With oxen the exchange takes place even faster than with human beings. New flesh is therefore made. From what did this flesh originate, however? You must ask yourselves this. The ox itself has produced the flesh in its body from plant substances. This is the most important point to consider. This animal's body is therefore capable of producing meat from plants. Now, you can cook cabbage as long as you like, but you won't turn it into meat! You do not produce meat in your frying pan or your stew pot, and nobody has ever baked a cake that became meat. This cannot be done with outer skills, but the animal's body can accomplish inwardly what one can't do outwardly. Flesh is produced in the animal's body, and forces to do this must first be present in the body. With all our technological forces, we have none by which we can simply produce meat from plants. We don't have that, but in our bodies and in animal bodies there are forces that can make meat substance from plant substance.

Now, this is a plant [sketching, see below] that is still in a meadow or field. The forces that have been active up to this point have brought forth green leaves, berries, and so forth. Imagine a cow devours this plant. When the cow devours this plant, it becomes flesh in her. This means that the cow possesses the forces that can make this plant into meat.

Now imagine that an ox suddenly decided that it was too tiresome to graze and nibble plants, that it would let another animal eat them and do the work for it, and then it would eat the animal. In other words, the ox would begin to eat meat, though it could produce the meat by itself. It has the inner forces to do so. What would happen if the ox were to eat meat directly instead of plants? It would leave all the forces unused that can produce the flesh in him. Think of the tremendous

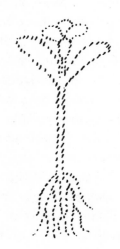

amount of energy that is lost when the machines in a factory in which something or other is manufactured are all turned on without producing anything. There is a tremendous loss of energy. But the unused energy in the ox's body cannot simply be lost, so the ox is finally filled with it, and this pent up force does something in him other than produce flesh from plant substances. It does something else in him. After all, the energy remains; it is present in the animal, and so it produces waste products. Instead of flesh, harmful substances are produced. Therefore, if an ox were suddenly to turn into a meat-eater, it would fill itself with all kinds of harmful substances such as uric acid and urates.

Now urates have their specific effects. The specific effects of urates are expressed in a particular affinity for the nervous system and the brain. The result is that if an ox were to consume meat directly, large amounts of urates would be secreted; they would enter the brain, and the ox would go crazy. If an experiment could be made in which a herd of oxen were suddenly fed with pigeons, it would produce a completely mad herd of oxen. That is what would happen. In spite of the gentleness of the pigeons, the oxen would go mad.

You see, such a matter naturally testifies against materialism, because if oxen only ate pigeons and if only the material element were effective, they would have to become as gentle as the pigeons. That would not be the case at all, however. Instead, the oxen would turn into terribly wild, furious creatures. This is proved by the fact that horses become extremely violent when fed a little meat. They begin to grow wild, because they are not accustomed to eating it.

This, of course, applies also to human beings. It is very interesting that historically a part of Asia's peoples is strictly vegetarian. These are gentle people who rarely wage war. In the Near East, people began to eat meat and thus brought about the madness of war. The peoples of the Asian nations transform plants into flesh by making use of the forces that otherwise are left unused, unconscious. Consequently, these people remain gentle whereas the meat-eaters of other nations do not remain so gentle.

We must be clear that people have only gradually become mature enough for such deliberations as we are presenting here. When people began to eat meat, it could not be considered in the way we have just done; it all arose from feeling and instinct.

You see, the lion continually devours meat; he is no plant eater. The lion also has very short intestines, unlike the plant-eating animals whose intestines are very long. This is also the case in humans. If a person is born into a certain race or people whose ancestors ate meat, then his intestines will already be shorter. They will be too short for pure vegetarianism. If, in spite of that, he eats only plants, he will have to practise all sorts of measures to remain healthy.

It is certainly possible to be a vegetarian today, and it has many points in its favour. One of the main advantages of eating only vegetables is that one does not tire as quickly. Since no uric acid and urates are secreted, one does not tire as quickly but will retain a clearer head and think more easily—if one is in the habit of thinking! A person who cannot think does not gain anything by freeing his brain from urates, because it is necessary for the whole human organization to harmonize. In any case, through self-control, a person can become a vegetarian today. Then he uses those forces that, in people who eat meat, are simply left unused . . .

We can therefore say that a meat diet produces unused forces in the human being that work in the human body improperly to produce waste. Naturally, this waste can then be eliminated again, but it is often a quite complicated task. One can say that when some matters are rightly expressed they look quite peculiar. Some people work in their own particular way all winter long and eat in their own way too. They consume with pleasure just enough food to give them a slight stomach upset every day, which they keep under control by drinking the necessary amount of alcohol. Come April or May they are ready for Karlsbad or some other health spa, since by that time they have accumulated a goodly amount of waste in their organisms, in their bodies. What they really need now is a thorough cleansing. The system must be cleaned out. They go to Karlsbad. You know that the waters of Karlsbad cause vigorous diarrhoea, which purges the system. This done, they can return home and begin all over again. As a rule, no more is necessary than to go to Karlsbad every year, but if they are kept from going once, they suffer from diabetes or some related problem.

From the standpoint of an affluent society, it does not sound too bad to say that so-and-so is going to Karlsbad. In reality, it means using manure buckets to put one's body back in order; this is what drinking the waters and taking the baths at Karlsbad accomplishes. The system is thoroughly purged and is then all right again for a while.

Naturally, this is no way to raise the level of national health. Ultimately, the quality of all foods processed and sold on the market is geared to the eating habits of a person who can afford to go to Karlsbad or a similar spa. One who cannot afford to go to Karlsbad also has to eat, but he can't be purged without the money. No other foods are available to him. Therefore we must start with medicine in order to set social life on the right course.

8. Potatoes, Beetroots, Radishes and the Spiritual in Human Beings

In this chapter Rudolf Steiner examines the effect of potatoes, beetroots and radishes in the context of how the body uses food to regenerate itself. Contrary to a materialistic view that it is food which directly builds the body, nutrition only provides the stimulus which enables the human being to regenerate himself out of the spiritual sphere.

Now I would still like to speak about something else, because that was also contained in one of your questions. You might be aware that potatoes were introduced to Europe at a particular time. Europeans have not always eaten potatoes...

If you look at the plant, it consists of roots, stem, leaves and blossom [a drawing is made]. It is a strange phenomenon in the plant: the root down there becomes very similar to the soil, containing many salts, and the blossom up there becomes very like the warm air. It is as if the warmth of the sun were continuously cooking the blossom. Hence the blossom contains oils and fats, oils in particular. So when we look at the plant, we have the salts below which are deposited. The root contains salts and the blossom contains oils.

Now the consequence of that is that when we eat roots we introduce many salts into our intestines. These salts find their way into the brain and stimulate the brain. And it is quite good if someone suffers from headache—not migraines but the kind of headache which fills the head—for them to eat

roots. You can taste how there is a kind of salty sourness in roots. When you eat the blossom, the plant is actually already half cooked. There we have the oils, something which lubricates the stomach and intestines and affects the abdomen. Doctors must also take that into account when they prescribe tea. You will never produce a strong effect on the head when you make tea from the blossom, but if you boil the roots and have the sick person drink that, there will be a strong effect on the head. So you see that whereas we must move from the stomach to the head in human beings, from below upwards, we must go in the opposite direction in plants, from the blossom to the root. The root of the plant is connected with the head. If we take that into consideration, we will understand the key thing about the potato. For the potato has tubers; they are something which has not quite become root. So if you eat potatoes a lot you are primarily eating vegetables which have not quite become root. Hence if you restrict yourself to eating potatoes and eat too many of them, not enough substance goes to the head. It remains below in the digestive tract. So we have a situation that through eating potatoes people in Europe have neglected their head, their brain. You will only see this connection once you start to engage in spiritual science. We might say that from the time that potatoes have taken an increasingly important place in Europe as a food the human head has lost in abilities.

Potatoes mainly stimulate the tongue and throat. When we go down the potato plant, we don't quite go as far as the root. The same happens in people; when we don't quite go up to the head and remain at the tongue and throat, they are particularly stimulated by the potato and that is why potatoes are very tasty as a side dish for people because they stimulate what lies below the head and leave the head alone.

If you eat beetroot, you get a terrible longing to think a lot. That happens to people quite unconsciously. When you eat potatoes, you get a longing to eat again quite soon. Potatoes make you hungry again so soon because they do not quite go as far as the head. Beetroot satisfies your hunger so quickly because it goes to the head, the most important thing, and because it infuses it with activity if it goes properly into the head. People sometimes find having to think terribly unpleasant and that is why they sometimes prefer potatoes to beetroot because potatoes don't stimulate them to think. They become lazy. Beetroot, by contrast, stimulates the thinking because it is a proper root, but it does so in a way which makes one want to think—but if one does not want to think, one won't like beetroot. If you need a stimulus for thinking, you need to use the salty stimulation of radishes, for example. If someone is not very mobile in their head, he will benefit from that because the thoughts are stimulated if the food is supplemented by radishes.

So you can see this remarkable situation that radishes stimulate the thinking. You don't even need to be very active in your thinking, strong thoughts will come when you eat radishes—such strong thoughts that they even produce powerful dreams. Anyone who eats many potatoes will not have powerful thoughts but dreams which will weigh him down. And so anyone who must constantly eat potatoes will actually always be tired and always want to sleep and dream. It is therefore of great significance in terms of cultural history what foods are provided for people.

You might say: but the situation is such that we live completely from matter! And yet that is not true. I have often told you that we human beings have a new body about every seven years. It is constantly renewing itself. What we had as matter in our body eight or ten years ago is no longer there. It has gone. We have cut it away with our nails, cut it off with the hair, it has gone as sweat. It has left. Some of it goes quite fast, some of it slowly, but it all goes.

You see, this is how these things are actually seen—let me draw a diagram: this is the human being. Now people are constantly shedding matter and are constantly taking in new matter. As a result, people think: matter enters through the mouth and leaves again through your rear and urine, people are rather like a tube. The matter is taken in through eating, it is kept for a while and ejected again. That is approximately how people see the human being.

But in fact nothing of earthly matter enters the real human being, nothing. That is a delusion. The situation is this, that when we eat potatoes, for example, then we are not assimilating something from the potato, but the potato

is merely something that stimulates our jaw and throat and so on. That is where the potato acts. And then the strength arises in us to expel the potato again and while we are expelling it we receive from the etheric, not from solid matter, what builds us up in the course of seven years. We do not actually build ourselves up from earthly matter. We only eat what we eat to stimulate us. In reality we are built up by what is up above. So that the whole thing which people imagine, that food goes in and that food goes out again and that in between something is left inside is not true; it only provides the stimulus. A reciprocal force comes from the etheric sphere and we build up the whole of our body from that realm. Nothing of which we are made up is built from earthly matter. You see, if there is a movement followed by a counter-movement you must not confuse the counter-movement with the movement. You must not confuse the fact that we need food to keep us active in building up our body with the fact that we consume food.

Now it is the case that irregularities can occur. Because if we take in too much food, then the food remains in us for too long. Then we collect more matter than necessary in us, become portly, fat and so on. If we take in too little, we have too little stimulation and take too little of what we need from the spiritual world, from the etheric world.

It is something of great importance that we do not build ourselves up from the earth and its substances, but that we construct ourselves from that which is outside the earth. If it is the case that the whole body is renewed in seven years, the heart is also renewed. You no longer have in you the heart which you bore within you eight years ago but it has been renewed, renewed not from the substance of the earth but renewed from what surrounds the earth in the light. Your heart is compacted light! You have indeed compacted your heart from the sunlight. And what you consumed as food only stimulated you to compact the sunlight to such an extent. All your organs are constructed from the light-imbued environment and we eat and consume nourishment to provide the stimulus.

You see, the only thing which food gives us is something like an inner armchair. We feel ourselves, experience ourselves as an ego in ordinary life, because we have physical matter in us. We feel ourselves in the same way as when you feel the pressure when you sit down in an armchair. And so you feel your body which continuously presses on what you have built from the cosmos. When you sleep you don't feel it, because you are outside yourself. You feel your body like a kind of recliner made for you, harder in some if they are bony, softer in others. It is like a kind of recliner on which the human being sits, and we do, after all, feel the difference between a soft bed and a wooden bench! Similarly human beings feel the difference between what is hard and soft within them. But that is not the real human being, the real human being is what sits in him.

9. The Effects of Protein, Fats, Carbohydrates and Salts

Here Rudolf Steiner looks specifically at the way that protein, fats, carbohydrates and salts affect the functions of the physical body and the spiritual parts of the human being. A particular aspect dealt with is the way that reproduction can be affected by an excessive diet of potatoes due to their negative nutritional effects, which have already been described in other parts of this book.

You will recall—I've already spoken about these things—that human beings really live off four types of product: protein, which they actually eat with all their foods but which is contained in a particularly characteristic form in chicken eggs. So that is the first thing, protein. Then human beings also eat fats, not just through the direct enjoyment of animal fats but fat is once again contained in all products. As you know, other products are also made into fat-containing products such as milk is made into cheese, and so on. The third food is those products which we describe as carbohydrates, and that is everything which we eat from the plant kingdom—of course we also eat it with other things but it is essentially contained in food such as wheat, rye, lentils, beans, but also potatoes, particularly in potatoes. The final thing that human beings require for life, which is normally considered to be an additive but which is essential for life, are the salts. Well, to begin with we mainly eat our salts in the form of cooking salt but, once again, all foods contain salts.

So we can say: in order for human beings to be able to live, their nutrition must consist of protein, fats, carbohydrates and salts.

Now I will describe to you what these various nutrients, which we get in various forms because we enjoy a mixed diet, mean for human beings. Let us start with the salts.

Salts are exceptionally important nutrients for human beings, even if they are only eaten in small quantities, and not just a luxury. We don't only salt our food so that we have, let us say, a certain sharpness of taste, but we salt our food so that we can think at all. As a nutrient, salt must penetrate as far as the brain if we are to be able to think at all. Salts are most closely connected with our thinking. If someone is so ill, for example, that all the salts in his food are deposited in the stomach or intestines and are not sent through the blood to the brain, he will become weak-minded, stupid. These are things to which attention must be drawn.

We must be clear about this: spirit exists, but spirit must work in matter if it is to be effective on earth. And, particularly in the pursuit of spiritual science, we must know the effect of the spirit in matter. Otherwise it would be like saying: making machinery is something material; but we are spiritual people, we don't want anything material, we don't want to buy iron and steel first, but we want to create machinery out of spirit. That is nonsense, of course. First you must have the materials. In the same way the creative spirit first needs matter everywhere in nature. And if it is prevented from using the material, if the salt is deposited in the stomach and intestines instead of penetrating to the brain through the blood, then people become stupid.

However, things are nevertheless not quite that simple. Human beings cannot use the salt directly in the form that it takes outside in nature. So if you were to make a small hole in the brain—something that is quite possible—and were to infuse the salt into the brain, that would be of no use whatsoever. The salt must enter the stomach because when it enters the stomach and intestines—observe that it has already been dissolved on the tongue—it is broken down even more finely, finer and finer. As a result of what happens to salt in the human being, it is already in a spiritualized state as it enters the brain. So the matter is not quite that simple, that we can directly take the salt to the brain. But anyone in whom the effect of salt in the brain is absent becomes stupid.

Now let us look at the carbohydrates. They are primarily in peas, beans, wheat, rye or potatoes; that is where we enjoy the carbohydrates. They contribute in particular to human beings having form. If we did not eat carbohydrates we would suffer all kinds of distortions in the human form. For example, the nose or the ears might not form properly. We would not have the human form we do. The effect of the carbohydrates is that we are externally recognizable as human beings. Their general effect is that we are recognizable everywhere as human beings. And if human beings are organized in such a way that the carbohydrates are not taken to the brain but are deposited in the intestines and stomach, then human beings deteriorate. Then one can see how a person collapses, how he sinks into himself, becomes weak and can no longer maintain his form. So the carbohydrates ensure that we have the proper human form at all.

You can see that the nutrients must be taken to their proper locations. The salts especially affect the front of the brain. Carbohydrates tend to work here towards the back of the brain, on this section here [a drawing was made]. And it would also soon turn out in human beings who cannot digest enough carbohydrates, who are not able to transfer them to this section of the brain, that they are constantly hoarse, that they cannot speak in a pure and clear way. So when you have a person who previously talked quite normally but now suddenly becomes hoarse you can say that there is something wrong with his digestion. He cannot digest carbohydrates in the proper way, they are not transferred to the correct section of the brain. This means that his breathing is no longer in order and nor is his speech. So we can say: the salts primarily affect the thinking. The carbohydrates work on speech, for example, and everything connected with it. It is necessary for us to have these carbohydrates.

Now you see, the carbohydrates work to create our form but they only work on the form. They do not fill it out. But we need to be filled out and that is done by the fats. So the fats have the effect that the form created by the carbohydrates, the plan drawn into the air, as we might describe it, is in turn filled with matter. The fats serve to ensure that we have matter in us in the proper way. That is expressed in a very special way through the fats.

I have told you previously that human beings have an I, an astral body, an etheric body and a physical body. The fat is, of course, deposited in the physical body but the most important thing which ensures that the fat can be deposited and remains alive—because we must have living fat in us—is the etheric body. That is the most important factor with regard to the deposit of fat. The astral body, in turn, is the most important factor for the senses.

When someone is awake the astral body is in him, when he is asleep it is removed. When a person is awake and the astral body works in the etheric body, the fat is continuously utilized. Everything in the body is lubricated through the fat.

When a person sleeps and the astral body is outside him, the fat is not utilized but deposited. When a person is awake, the fat is constantly used for lubrication, when asleep it is deposited. We need both, the fat which is deposited and the fat which is used for lubricating the body.

It can, of course, also happen that a person is not able to deposit fat properly, that he is ill. It may be that the fats cannot be deposited properly and are expelled with the faeces, with the result that we have too little fat for lubrication. Or if we simply have too little food, are starving, we cannot lubricate sufficiently. It is, after all, the fat which we place into the body. What happens when a person either has to suffer hunger or his digestion is such that he cannot deposit the fat but it is expelled through the faeces? Such a person, who has no matter in his body, becomes increasingly spiritual. But human beings are not made to become spiritual in this way. The spirit burns up. Not only does the person become more and more scrawny, but gases form in him resulting in delusions and similar things. Illness is always a destruction of the body. So that if a person gets too little fat something occurs which we might describe as wasting away, consumption it is also called; the person wastes away.

Now if we take protein. You see, it has to be there right from the beginning. Protein already exists in egg form before the entity is there, the human or animal entity. So we can say that it is the protein which actually forms, develops the human being; it is what is there originally, the underlying substance. Everything else in the body develops out of the protein. So we can say the following: protein has to be there from the beginning in order for the human being to be created. The mother forms the protein in the uterus in the form of a small lump. The egg is fertilized and this fertilization then enables the protein to develop into a human being by means of the things which I have described. But of course human beings continue to need protein. Hence their nourishment must continue to include protein. If they have too little protein or if the protein cannot be properly digested, they not only waste away from lack of protein—which would eventually kill them—but if human beings at some point in their lives had no proper protein at all they would die immediately. Just as protein is necessary when the human being is created, it is necessary for the human being to live at all. So we can say that death would occur in any person who was totally unable to digest protein.

Now let us take a look at these individual nutrients. When we look at the salts, we are primarily directed to the front part of the head. That is where the salts are deposited. The carbohydrates are deposited slightly further back with the effect that we have our human form. The fats are deposited still further back and from there fill the body because the fats do not enter the body directly but go to the head through the blood and only there are they utilized for the body. Everything goes through the head, including protein.

There are, however, huge differences as far as the carbohydrates are concerned. When you consider something like lentils, beans, peas, rye and corn, you can say that the carbohydrates here are acquired from fruits. Because what we have from the earth in wheat is the fruit. With lentils that is also the fruit. You see, fruits have the characteristic that they are already digested in the stomach and the gut and only their forces are sent to the head. Everybody knows that lentils, beans are processed in the intestines through the particular results which occur when lentils and beans are enjoyed. All these things, corn, wheat, lentils, beans, are processed in the gut. So the fruits have the main characteristic that they are already properly processed in the gut.

In potatoes, however, we cannot enjoy the fruit. If we ate what is the fruit in potatoes, we would be eating poison. We cannot eat potatoes in the same way as we do lentils, beans, peas and so on or field crops such as rye and wheat. Because what do we eat in the potato? We eat what is down below, the tuber. And the tuber is that part in all plants, roots and so on, which is processed least in the intestines.

If we now look at the structure of the human being, we have to say that the physical body initially originates in protein. This protein is connected with the birth and death of the physical human being. The main field of the etheric body lies in the fats. The astral body has its main field in the carbohydrates and only the I has its field in the salts.

So we can say that everything which is sentient capacity in the human being is connected with the astral body—not the physical body, such as when I hit my hand for example, because otherwise everything physical would have sensation. I move the flesh, the muscle, pushing it out of the astral body, and that sensation then occurs in the astral body. Everything which is inner sensation occurs in the astral body. But the astral body is dependent on working properly. I told you that if the astral body also sleeps during the day and cannot work properly, a paunch, fat, is deposited. Or alternatively if a person works only intellectually with his head, fat is deposited. But the astral body, which also works partly in speech, needs carbohydrates not only up in the head but in the whole body. The astral body must move the legs, the astral body must move the hands, it needs carbohydrates in the whole body. If I give it rye or wheat as carbohydrates, the forces go into the whole body. If I only give it potatoes, the forces remain seated in the head and the human being becomes emaciated, weak, and his astral body cannot work properly. Then precisely those things in the human being which are of a spiritual nature become exhausted and increasingly sleepy if it is not able to take into itself carbohydrates which penetrate the whole person. If only potatoes are consumed, that is not possible because they create such a lot of work in the head that the body does not retain anything.

We might well ask what role science plays in all this. Well, science investigates how much carbon, oxygen, nitrogen, hydrogen, sulphur and similar things are contained in protein. So science discovers that protein contains a certain percentage of carbon, a certain percentage of hydrogen, fat contains other percentages, carbohydrates other percentages again. But science has no idea what the meaning of these substances is as such. It only knows the percentages of the constituents. But you cannot do anything with that. It is simply the case that the constituents are quite different in the potato and in rye and wheat, and one has to know that if one eats blossoms or a fruit they are processed in the intestines whereas if one eats a root it is processed in the head . . .

But we can go further and say: but what if human beings not only become emaciated through eating potatoes to such an extent that they can no longer move their hands and feet, but to such an extent that those things are no longer active which are required for reproduction? Then the whole thing becomes even worse. Let us assume that potatoes as nutrition have become so dominant that they affect the female reproductive organs, that they become weak and inactive. Human beings do not come only from their ancestors but they come from the spiritual world with the soul-spiritual part of their being and that is combined with what comes from our

ancestors. So let us look at what is really happening. I will
draw it quite large, a bit enlarged.

We can say that the human being develops from the female
egg cell. This is drawn very much enlarged. This is penetrated by the male sperm. Then all kinds of star-shaped forms
develop. Cells divide which gradually form the human body.
But no human body can be formed if it is not united with the
soul-spiritual element which comes from the spiritual world.

If the parents have eaten too many potatoes, a human
embryo develops which has a predisposition that the head
must work a lot. So if you look at a human embryo from
someone who is properly nourished with rye bread and so on,
where the parents had the right kind of food, the human
embryo is something like this [a drawing was made]. But if
you look at a human embryo where the parents fed themselves too much on potatoes, the following happens. The
round sphere of the head is primarily developed while the
remainder of the embryo is less developed. Now the soul-
spiritual element must enter the head. And when the soul-
spiritual element enters the head, it must work with the head.
The soul-spiritual element works primarily in the head while
it is still in the body of the mother.

If this soul-spiritual element now finds in the head what
comes from rye and wheat in the nutrition of the mother,
then the soul-spiritual element can work properly. Because
the blossoms in which the rye and wheat and so on arise are
extended out of the earth and allow contact with the spirit.
They are related to the spirit. So when the soul-spiritual
element in the womb encounters what comes from fruits, it
can work easily. But if the soul-spiritual element encounters a
child's head in the womb which has been primarily formed
through potato nourishment, it has no access. After all, the

potato goes down into the earth, it is even covered by earth; it is dug out of the ground and grows in darkness, it has no affinity with the spirit. The human being comes from the spiritual world and finds a head which has really been formed from darkness. The spirit cannot access that and the consequence is that the embryo later looks like this [a drawing was made]—I am exaggerating slightly—a giant hydrocephalus is born. Because if the physical element grows without access by the spirit it just grows and a hydrocephalus develops. If the spirit can have access it curbs the water, then the spirit works in matter and the head is properly developed. So you can say that these giant heads which are often apparent in embryos arise from deficient nourishment, particularly with regard to potatoes. And so you have a situation where not only people themselves are emaciated, but the human being is born such that his soul-spiritual element has not properly entered the physical body.

You see, the situation is like this. The human being consists of a physical body, etheric body, astral body and the I, but they change at various ages. In the child up to age seven the etheric body, astral body and the I are such that they have to fully immerse themselves in the physical body. Once the etheric body has fully entered the physical body, the child gets his second set of teeth. Once the astral body has entered the physical body, sexual maturity occurs. If, then, we have a head in which the soul-spiritual element was not able to enter properly into the physical person in the womb because of a diet of potatoes, then what is supposed to happen at age 14, 15 is also disrupted. The person then goes through life as if he did not have his body, as if it were fatigued. So that the influence of a potato diet means that the human being is not even born strong enough for life.

These things are incredibly important. It is true to say that the social conditions depend on many more factors than are normally proclaimed today. The social conditions are dependent on the fields being properly used so that only such quantities of potatoes are planted as are needed by humans to make them strong. Real, true science must be pursued alongside social science. Simply to talk about added value, capital is no use. Let us just assume that Communism succeeded in getting rid of all capital and managed everything itself. But if it has only learned traditional science which does not know how to manage the fields in a proper way, if it does not know that it is more harmful to fill you stomach with potatoes than with rye and wheat, then nothing else will help either. That is what we must consider. We don't need the constant discussions of this and that, but a real science which recognizes how the spirit works in matter . . .

Now you might well say that not everyone walks around with a hydrocephalus. Of course not, because other forces counter it and once the baby is born the head is no longer as large as it was when it was an embryo. But once it is born it is no longer capable of assimilating anything other than potatoes and water. It can even become small and still be a hydrocephalus. The key point is that since the introduction of the potato diet the heads in the womb are always much too large. Later they are compressed, but precisely such compression before birth has a harmful effect because they are no longer able to assimilate things properly other than materialistic things. Once a person is born, one can no longer see the hydrocephalus only by its size. True, the actual hydrocephalus is dependent on the size, but the important point is whether or not water or something else can work in the correct way. And it is just as important to know this as everything else which humankind learns about—on the one hand through science and on the other hand through theology and religion. It is indeed necessary to look at things properly.

10. The Effects of Alcohol

While people's attitude towards smoking has changed significantly, with the health risks it entails generally recognized and accepted, the same has not happened with alcohol. The rise in binge drinking in Britain, for example, particularly among young people, illustrates that the health risks of excessive alcohol consumption are still widely ignored. Rudolf Steiner here sets out what some of those risks are.

A question is asked concerning alcohol, its negative effects, etc. Do you mean the extent to which alcohol generally is detrimental to health? Well, alcohol's initial effect is quite obvious, because it influences what we have been describing in the human being all along, that is, the entire constitution of the soul. In the first place, through alcohol, a person suffers a form of spiritual confusion so strong that he becomes subject to passions that otherwise are weak in him and can easily be suppressed by his reason. A person thus appears more sensible if he has had no alcohol than if he drinks. To begin with, alcohol has a stimulating influence on the blood, causing increased blood circulation. This, in turn, arouses a person's passions; for example, he may more readily become furious, whereas otherwise he can control his anger more easily. So you can see that the first effect of alcohol is exercised on the human being's reason—indeed, on his whole life of soul.

After alcohol has remained for a certain length of time in

the organism, it causes another symptom that you know well, hangover; the appearance of a hangover shows you that the entire organism objects to the initial effect of alcohol. What does it mean for a person to have a hangover? As a rule, it appears in the morning after an evening of too much drinking. Due to the drinking the night before, the circulation of a person's blood is strongly agitated. The increased movement that otherwise would have taken its course at a much slower pace uses up a lot of energy.

Pay close attention to this! Let us assume that the body accomplishes a certain activity within 24 hours. When somebody consumes a goodly amount of alcohol, the same activity is completed in perhaps twelve or even six hours. The body thus deprives itself of inner activity. People who are in the habit of drinking every once in a while, therefore, instinctively do something before the hangover appears: they eat heartily. Why do they do this? They eat heartily either to avoid a hangover altogether or so that its effects the next day are at least milder, so that they can work.

What happens if a person has drunk himself into a visible state of intoxication and then consumes, let's say, a large hot dog? He stimulates again what has been used up by the previous excessive activity. But if, because he is not a habitual drinker, he doesn't do this—habitual drinkers remember to eat—and he forgets to eat that hot dog, he then will suffer the hangover, basically because his body is no longer able to engage in increased inner activity. When the body does not function correctly, however, waste products, in particular uric acid, are deposited everywhere. Since the head is the most difficult to supply, the waste products are deposited there. If a person has, through alcohol consumption, depleted the inner activity of the body during the night, he walks around the next morning with his head in the condition that is normal for his intestines, that is, filled with refuse. An immediate revolt by the body is brought about when, through the intake of alcohol, too much activity is demanded of it.

As I have mentioned to you before in these lectures, the human being has a much higher tolerance—I don't mean only regarding alcohol but generally—and can take much more abuse than is normally assumed. He is capable of readjustment for a long time. Some people even make use of a most deceptive, most questionable antidote against a hangover. When they come home or get up the next morning with a powerful hangover, what do they do? Surely you have seen this; they continue drinking, making the morning pint into a special cure.

What does this continued drinking signify? During the night, through the agitation of the blood, the body has been deprived of functioning activity. This activity is now missing in the morning. Through renewed drinking, the body is stimulated once again, so that the last remnants of activity are also consumed. Since, with these last remnants, the major part of the refuse is also disposed of, the hangover disappears to a degree from the head but remains that much more in the rest of the body. People are, however, less aware of that. Additional drinking in the morning thus unconsciously transfers the hangover to the rest of the organism. Only now, when this occurs, does the real misery for the body begin. Those alcoholics who drive away a hangover with more drinking are in the worst shape, because gradually, as this is repeated, the entire body is ruined.

Still, however, because the human being can endure a good deal, it is almost impossible to ruin the body that quickly. Therefore the first thing that happens to a real alcoholic is that he suffers from a form of delirium. This does not as yet indicate total ruin. When delirium tremens, as it is called in medicine, sets in, people see certain kinds of animals, mice and the like, running all over the place. They suffer a form of persecution complex. Delirium tremens is connected with the phenomenon of people seeing themselves surrounded and attacked from all sides by small animals, especially mice. This is something that even has a historical background. There are structures called 'mice towers' which have usually come by their name through somebody in some earlier time having been incarcerated in them who suffered from delirium tremens; and, though some real mice might well have been there too, this person was plagued by thousands upon thousands of mice that he merely imagined all around himself.

You can see, therefore, that the effects of alcohol can only very slowly ruin the body; the body resists these alcohol-induced effects for a long time.

What happens when people who have been drinking heavily for some time are suddenly bothered by their conscience and, having some energy left, stop drinking? It is an interesting fact that if they had not suffered from delirium tremens before, now, after abstaining from alcohol, they sometimes get it. Here we find something of interest, when people's consciences suddenly stir. They have been drinking for a while, let us say, drinking since early in the morning, and then suddenly their conscience stirs and they stop drinking. What happens then? If they had not had delirium tremens earlier, they struggle with it now. This is the interesting fact, that sometimes those who have been drinking for a long time begin suffering from delirium tremens when they stop drinking.

This is one of the most important signs that the human being must be viewed in such a way that the head is seen to work differently from the rest of the body. In the last lectures I mentioned many aspects of this to you. As long as a person suffers only in his head from the side-effects of drinking, his overall condition is still tolerable; the effects have not yet permeated the entire body. When they have penetrated, however, and the person gives up alcohol, the rest of the body really revolts by way of the brain and he suffers from delirium tremens just because he discontinued drinking.

One thus can say that it is the blood which bears the bodily counterpart for the most important functions of the soul. You probably know that some people suffer from persecution complexes, seeing all sorts of figures that are not there. Particularly in earlier times, such persons were bled—not a bad remedy, really. You must not believe that all people in the past were as superstitious as is generally assumed today. Bloodletting was not something derived from superstition. People were bled primarily by applying leeches somewhere on the body that drew off blood. The blood thus became less active. Not necessarily in the case of alcoholics, but for other attacks of insanity the blood thus became less active and the person fared better.

As I have mentioned, the nervous system is very closely related to the foundations of our properties of soul, but it is much less important for the human will. The nervous system is important for reason, but for the human will it has much less significance than the blood.

Now, when you see that alcohol pre-eminently attacks the blood, it is clear from the body's strong reaction to alcohol's effects that the blood is well protected against alcohol. The blood is extraordinarily well protected against the assault of alcohol on human beings. By what means is the blood so strongly protected against this assault? We must ask further, then. Where do the most important ingredients of the blood actually originate?

Remember that I told you that blood consists of red corpuscles containing iron, which swim around in the so-called blood serum, and it also consists of white corpuscles. I told you that the most significant components of blood are the red and white corpuscles. We shall now disregard the corpuscles connected with the spleen's activity, which, in our tests in Stuttgart, we termed the 'regulators'. There are many components in the blood, but we want now to focus only on the red and white corpuscles, asking where in the body these corpuscles originate. These corpuscles originate in a most special place. If you examine the thigh bone from the hip to the knee, if you think of the bone in the arm, or any long bone, you will find in these bones the so-called bone marrow. The marrow is in there, the bone marrow. And you see, gentlemen, the red and white corpuscles originate in this bone marrow and migrate from it first into the arteries. The human body is arranged in such a way that the blood, at least the most important part of it, is produced in the inner hollows of the bones.

If this is the case, you can say to yourself: in so far as its production is concerned, the blood is indeed well protected from harm. In fact, alcohol must be consumed for a long time and in large quantities to damage the bone to the point of penetrating it to the innermost part, to the bone marrow, and destroying the bone marrow so that no more red and white corpuscles are produced. Only then, after the effects of drinking alcohol have reached the bone marrow, does the really ruinous process begin for the human being.

Now it is true that regarding their intellects and soul qualities human beings are in many ways alike. Regarding the blood, however, there is a marked difference between man and woman. It is a difference that one is not always aware of, but that is nevertheless clearly evident. This is that the influence on human beings of the red and white corpuscles that are produced within the hollows of the bone is such that the red corpuscles are more important for the woman and the white are more important for the man. This is very important: the red corpuscles are more important with the woman and the white with the man.

This is because the woman, as you know, has her menstrual period every four weeks, which is actually an activity that the human body undertakes to eliminate something that must be eliminated, red corpuscles. A man, however, does not have menstrual periods, and you can easily tell that his semen is not derived directly from red blood. It has its origin in white corpuscles. Although considerably transformed, in the end they turn into the main ingredient of semen. Thus, regarding what affects human reproduction, we must go to the protected bone marrow to investigate the means by which the human reproductive capacity can be influenced physically. Indeed, the human reproductive capacity can be physically affected precisely through the bone marrow within the bone.

After having been produced in the bone marrow, the red and white corpuscles naturally enter the bloodstream. When a woman now drinks alcohol, it is the red corpuscles that are particularly affected. The red corpuscles contain iron, are somewhat heavy, and possess something of the earth's heaviness. When a woman drinks, it affects her in such a way that there is too much heaviness in her. When a pregnant woman drinks, therefore, her developing child becomes too heavy and cannot inwardly form its organs properly. It does not develop properly inwardly, and its inner organs are not in order. In this roundabout way, gentlemen, the harmful influence of alcohol is expressed in the woman.

In men, alcohol primarily affects the white corpuscles. If conception takes place when a man is under the influence of alcohol, or when his system is generally contaminated by the effects of alcoholism, a man's semen is ruined in a way, becoming too restless. When conception takes place, the tiny egg is released from the mother's organism. This can only be seen with a microscope. From the male, a great number of microscopic sperm are released, each one of which has something resembling a tail attached to it. The seminal fluid contains countless numbers of such sperm. This tail, which is like a fine hair, gives the sperm great restlessness. They make the most complicated movements, and naturally one sperm must reach the egg first. The one that reaches the egg first penetrates it. The sperm is much smaller than the egg. Although the egg can be perceived only with a microscope, the sperm is still smaller. As soon as the egg has received it, a membrane forms around the egg, thereby preventing penetration by the rest of the sperm cells. Generally only one sperm can enter the egg. As soon as one has penetrated, a membrane is formed around the egg, and the others must retreat.

You see, therefore, it is most ingeniously arranged. Now, the sperm's restlessness is greatly increased through alcohol, so that conception occurs under the influence of semen that is extraordinarily lively. If the father is a heavy drinker when conception occurs, the child's nerve-sense system will be affected. The woman's drinking harms the child's inner organs because of the heaviness that ensues. The man's drinking harms the child's nervous system. All the activities are damaged that should be present in the right way as the child grows up.

We can therefore say that if a woman drinks, the earthly element in the human being is ruined; if a man drinks, the element of movement, the airy element that fills the earth's surroundings and that the human being carries within himself, is ruined. When both parents drink, therefore, the embryo is harmed from two different sides. Naturally conception is still possible, but proper growth of the embryo is not. On the one hand, the egg's tendency towards heaviness tries to prevail; on the other, everything in it is in restless motion, and one tendency contradicts the other. If both parents are alcoholics and conception occurs, the masculine element contradicts the feminine. To those who understand the entire relationship, it becomes quite clear that in the case of habitual drinkers exceedingly harmful elements actually arise in their offspring. People do not wish to believe this, because the effects of heavy drinking in men and women are not so obvious, relatively speaking. This is only because the blood is so well protected, however, being produced, after all, in the bone marrow, and because people must do a lot if they are to affect their offspring strongly. Weak effects are simply not admitted by people today.

As a rule, if a child is born with water on the brain, one does not investigate whether or not, on the night conception occurred, the mother was at a dinner party where she drank red wine. If that were done, it would often be found to be the case, because wine causes an inclination towards heaviness, so that the child can be born with hydrocephalus. If, however, the baby has a congenital twitch in a facial muscle, one normally does not check to find out if the father had perhaps been drinking too much the evening conception occurred. Seemingly insignificant matters are not investigated; people therefore assume that they have no effect. Actually, alcohol always has an effect. The really disastrous effects, however, occur with habitual drinkers. Here, too, a striking, a very remarkable thing can be noted.

You see, the children of a father who drinks can develop a weakness somewhere in their nervous systems and thus have a tendency towards tuberculosis, for example. What is inherited by the children need not be connected with the effects felt by the alcoholic father. The children need not have a tendency towards mental confusion, for example, but instead, towards tuberculosis, stomach ailments, and the like. This is what is so insidious about the effects of alcohol, that they are passed on to totally different organs in human beings of the next generation.

In these matters, the great effect on human development of minute amounts of substances must always be taken into consideration. Not only that, but in each instance one must consider how these substances are introduced into the human being. Consider the following example. Our bones contain a certain amount of calcium phosphate. Our brain also contains some phosphorus, and you will recall from earlier lectures that phosphorus is most useful since without phosphorus the brain actually could not be used for thinking. We therefore have phosphorus in us. I have already told you that phosphorus has a beneficial effect when the proper amount is consumed in food so that it is digested at a normal rate. If too large an amount of phosphorus is introduced too quickly into the human stomach, it is not useful but instead harmful.

Something else must also be considered, however. You know that in earlier days matches were made with heads of phosphorus, but they are rarely seen any more. When I was 13, 14 and 15 years old, I had an hour's walk from our home to school every day. There was a match factory about half-way where phosphorus matches were manufactured by workmen. At any time, one could see that a number of these workmen had corroded jaws—this was in the 1870s—and, starting from the jaw, their bodies were gradually destroyed. Beginning with the upper and lower jaws—especially the upper—the bones were eaten away.

Knowing the harmful effect that phosphorus can have on people, one realizes that such a match factory is actually about the most murderous place there is. In matters connected with the progress of human civilization, it is always necessary to look at the numerous harmful effects that people can suffer in this way. I always saw a number of these workmen going into this match factory with bandaged jaws. That is where it started, and then it spread. Of course, phosphorus was obviously already contained in the upper jawbone, but what kind of phosphorus was it?

You see, the phosphorus that first enters the stomach along with food and then travels internally through the body into the jaws is not harmful, provided the amount is not too large. Matches, however, are manufactured first by cutting long wooden strips into tiny sticks; these are then fitted into frames so that one end sticks out. They are dipped first into a sulphur solution and then into a phosphorus solution. The workman who dipped the matches simply held the frame in his hand and always got splattered. Just think how often in a day a person who cannot wash his splattered hands might touch his face during working hours. Though the amounts of phosphorus with which the person comes in contact in this way are minute, they nevertheless penetrate his skin. This is a mystery of human nature. A substance that is often extraordinarily useful when taken internally and assimilated first through the body can have the most poisonous effect when it comes in contact with the body from outside. The human organism is so wisely arranged inwardly that an overdose of phosphorus is eliminated in the urine or faeces; only the small amount required is allowed to penetrate the bones, the rest is eliminated.

There are, however, no provisions for the elimination of externally absorbed influences. This problem could, of course, have been alleviated. Remember that in the last century little thought was given to humanitarian considerations. It would have helped if bathing facilities had been made available so that every workman could have had a hot bath before leaving work. A great deal could naturally have been accomplished by such an arrangement, but it simply was not done.

I only mention this to you to illustrate how the human body works. Minute, detrimental influences from outside, even substances that the body otherwise needs to sustain itself, can undermine human health, indeed, can generally undermine the entire organization of the human being.

The human being can withstand a good deal, but beyond a certain point the organism fails. In the case of drinking alcohol, the organism fails at the point at which alcohol prevents the correct functioning of life-sustaining activities, the invisible life-sustaining activities.

When a person is exposed to phosphorus poisoning, the inner activity that otherwise would assimilate phosphorus is undermined. It is undermined from outside. It is actually quite similar in the case of alcohol. When a person drinks too much alcohol, drinking always more and more, so that imbibing alcohol is no longer merely acute but has become chronic, the alcohol works directly as alcohol in the human being. What is the direct effect of alcohol? Remember that I once told you that the human being himself produced the amount of alcohol he requires. I told you that in the substances contained in the intestines a certain amount of alcohol is constantly produced by ordinary food, simply because the human being needs this small amount of alcohol. What do we need it for? Remember that in an anatomy lab specimens are preserved in alcohol, because otherwise they would decompose. The alcohol prevents what was a living body from decaying. The alcohol produced in the human being works in the same way in the human organism; that is, it prevents decay of certain substances needed by the human being. The human being's inner organization really prescribes how much alcohol he should have, because he has certain substances that would otherwise decay and must be conserved.

Take now the case of a person who drinks too much alcohol. Substances that should be eliminated are retained in the body; too much is preserved. If a person repeatedly exposes blood that circulates in the body to alcohol, he conserves this blood in his body. What is the consequence? This blood, having a counteracting influence, blocks the canals in the bones; it is not eliminated quickly enough through the pores and so forth. It remains too long in the body. The marrow in the hollows of the bone is consequently stimulated too little to make new blood, and it becomes weak. It so happens that, in the so-called chronic alcoholic, the bone marrow in time becomes weakened and no longer produces either the proper red corpuscles in the woman nor the proper white corpuscles in the man.

Now, at a point such as this, I always have to make the following observation. Certainly, it is very nice when people come up with social reforms such as the prohibition of alcohol and so forth. It certainly sounds fine. But even such a learned man as Professor Benedict—I told you about his collection of criminals' skulls and how Hungarian convicts objected to having their skulls sent to Vienna because they would be missing from the rest of their bones on Judgment Day—even Professor Benedict said, and rightly so, 'Here people speak against alcohol, but many more have perished from water than from alcohol.' Generally, that is quite correct, because water, if it is contaminated, can be present in much larger quantities. Considered simply from a statistical point of view one can naturally say that many more people have died from water than from alcohol.

Something else must be taken into consideration, however. I would like to put it like this. The situation with alcohol is like the story contained in Heinrich Seidel's *Leberecht Hühnchen*. I don't know whether you are familiar with it, but it is the tale of a poor wretch, a poor devil who only has enough money to buy one egg. He also has a great imagination, however, and so he thinks, 'If this egg had not been sold in the store but instead had been allowed to hatch, a hen would have developed from it. Now, when I eat this egg, I am actually eating a whole hen.' And so he imagines, 'Why, I, who have a whole hen to eat, am really a rich fellow!' But his imagination is not satisfied there, so he continues, 'Yes, but the hen I am now eating could have laid any number of eggs from which hens again would hatch, and I am eating all these hens.' Finally, he calculates how many millions and millions of hens that would amount to, and he asks himself, 'Shouldn't that be called gorging myself with food?'

You see, this is the case with alcohol, not in a funny sense as in this story but in all seriousness. Certainly, if you take the time from 1870 to 1880, and you investigate how many people died throughout the world from water and from alcohol, statistics would show that more people died from impure water. In those days, people died more frequently from typhoid fever and related illnesses than today, and typhoid can, in many instances, be traced to contamination of the water. So, in this way, gentlemen, it is easy to conclude that more people die from drinking water.

One must think differently, however. One must know that alcohol gradually penetrates the bone marrow and ruins the blood. By harming the offspring, all the descendants are thus harmed. If an alcoholic has three children, for example, these three are harmed only a little; their descendants, however, are significantly hurt. Alcohol has a long-term negative effect that manifests in many generations. Much of the weakness that exists in humanity today is simply due to ancestors who drank too much. One must indeed picture it like this: here is a man and a woman, the man drinks too much, and the bodies of their descendants are weakened. Now think for a moment what this implies in a hundred, and worse, in several hundred years! It serves no purpose to examine only a decade, say from 1870 to 1880, and to conclude that more people died from water than from alcohol. Much longer periods of time must be considered. This is something that people don't like to do nowadays, except in jest as did the author of *Leberecht Hühnchen*, who naturally was looking over a long span of time when picturing how to wallow in so much food.

If this matter is examined from the social viewpoint, consideration must go beyond what is nearest at hand. Now the use of alcohol can be prohibited, but when it is, strange phenomena appear. You know, for example, that in many parts of the world the sale of alcohol has been restricted or even completely prohibited. But I call your attention to another evil that has recently made its appearance in Europe, that is, the use of cocaine by people who wish to intoxicate themselves. In comparison to what the use of cocaine will do, particularly in damage to the human reproductive forces, alcohol is benign! Those individuals who take cocaine do not hold cocaine responsible for the damage it does, but you can see from the external symptoms that its use is much worse than that of alcohol. When a person suffers from delirium tremens, it becomes manifest in a form of persecution complex. He sees mice everywhere that pursue him. A cocaine user, however, imagines snakes emerging everywhere from his body [see drawing on next page]. First, such a person seeks an escape through cocaine, and for a while he feels good inside, because it brings about a feeling of sensual pleasure. When he has not had any cocaine for some time, however, and he looks at himself, he sees snakes emerging everywhere from his body. Then he runs to have another dose of cocaine so that the snakes will leave him alone for a while. The fear he has of these snakes is much greater than the fear of mice that is experienced by an alcoholic suffering from delirium tremens.

Certainly, one can prohibit this or that, but people then hit on something else, which as a rule is not better but much worse. I therefore believe that enlightening explanations, like the one we presented today regarding the effects of alcohol, for example, can be much more effective and will gradually

bring human beings to refrain from alcohol on their own. This does not infringe on human freedom, but understanding causes a person to say to himself, 'Why, this is shocking! I am harmed right into my bones!' This becomes effective as feeling, whereas laws work only on the intellect. The real truths, the real insights, are those that work all the way into feeling. It is therefore my conviction that we can arrive at an effective social reform—and in other spheres it is much the same—only if true enlightenment in the widest circles of people is made our concern.

This enlightenment, however, can come about only when there is something with which one can enlighten people. When a lecture is given nowadays on the detrimental effects of alcohol, these things are not presented as I have done today—though that should not be so difficult, because people know the facts. But they do not know how to think correctly about these facts that are familiar to them. The listeners come away from a lecture given by some dime-a-dozen professor, and they do not know quite what to make of it. If they are particularly good-natured, they might say, 'Well, we don't have the background to comprehend everything he said. The educated gentleman knows it all. A simple person can't understand everything!' The fact is that the lecturer himself doesn't fully comprehend what he is talking about. If one has a science that really goes to the root of things and considers their underlying foundations, however, it is possible to make it comprehensible even to simple people.

If science is so unreal today, it is because true humanness was excluded from it when it originated. Teachers at the universities can rise from lecturer to assistant professor, in Germany from 'extraordinary professor' to full professor. The students are in the habit of saying, 'The full professor knows nothing extraordinary, and the assistant professor knows nothing fully.' The students sense this in their feelings, gentlemen; the sorry state of affairs thus continues. Regarding social reforms, science essentially accomplishes nothing, whereas it could be effective in the most active way. A person who is sincerely concerned about social life therefore must emphasize again and again that dry laws on paper are much less important—though naturally they too are needed—but they are much less important than thorough enlightenment. The public needs this enlightenment; then we would have real progress.

Particularly facts like those that can be studied in the case of alcohol can be made comprehensible everywhere. One then arrives at what I always tell people. People come and ask, 'Is it better not to drink alcohol or is it better to drink it? Is it better to be a vegetarian or to eat meat?' I never tell anyone whether or not he should abstain from alcohol, or whether he should eat vegetables or meat. Instead, I explain how alcohol works. I simply describe how it works; then the person may decide to drink or not as he pleases. I do the same regarding vegetarian or meat diets. I simply say, this is how meat works and this is how plants work. The result is that a person can then decide for himself.

Above all else, science must have respect for human freedom, so that a person never has the feeling of being given orders or forbidden to do something. He is only told the facts. Once he knows how alcohol works, he will discover on his own what is right. This way we shall accomplish the most. We will come to the point where free human beings can choose their own directions. We must strive for this. Only then will we have real social reforms.

11. The Effects of Nicotine

The various risks associated with smoking are well recognized today. Speaking in the early years of the last century, Rudolf Steiner explains the subtle effects of nicotine on the human organism, generally negative but, under certain circumstances, also positive. As always, Steiner is not seeking to be prescriptive but to inform so that each person can weigh up the risks and take the appropriate decision for himself or herself.

Now we shall try to go into these questions. The first asked about the influence of nicotine and therefore of the poison that is introduced into the human body through smoking and through tobacco in general. First, we must be clear how the effect of nicotine shows itself. The effect of nicotine shows itself above all in the activity of the heart. Through nicotine, an increased, stronger activity of the heart is called forth. The heart is not a pump, however, but only reflects what goes on in the body: the heart beats faster when the blood circulates faster. Nicotine therefore actually affects the blood circulation, animating it. One must therefore be clear that through the introduction of nicotine into the human body the blood circulation is stimulated. This, in turn, calls forth a stronger activity of the heart.

Now, this whole process in the human organism must be traced. You must be clear that everything occurring in the human organism is actually carefully regulated. One of the most important points regarding the human organism, for example, is the fact that the pulse rate of the adult is 72 beats a minute, and this holds true even into old age.

By comparison, as I have mentioned to you before, the human being takes about 18 breaths a minute. When you multiply 18 by 4, you get 72. This means that on average the blood pulses four times as quickly through the body as does the breath. Of course, these are average figures; they differ slightly in each human being. The fact that this ratio varies in people accounts for the differences between them, but on average it is 1:4; that is, the blood circulation is four times more intense than that of the breathing rhythm.

If I now introduce nicotine into the human organism, I can do it for two reasons—first because of a strong liking for tobacco, and second as a remedy. Every substance that is poisonous is also a remedy. Everything, one can say, is both poisonous and healing. If, for example, you drink several buckets of water, they naturally have a poisonous effect, whereas the proper amount is a means of sustenance. And when it is introduced in unusually small amounts, it can even be a remedy. As a matter of fact, water is generally a potent remedy when certain methods are employed. It can therefore be said that even the most commonplace substances can be poisons as well as remedies. This is why the effect that a given substance has on the human organism must be known.

If I introduce tobacco into the human organism, it first stimulates the blood circulation. The blood becomes more active, circulating more vigorously. Breathing, however, is not stimulated to the same degree by tobacco; the breathing rhythm remains the same. The blood circulation is therefore no longer synchronized with the breathing. When people introduce nicotine into their bodies, they really need a blood circulation different from the one they normally have.

Let us, for example, imagine someone whose system was adjusted to the exact average of 18 breaths and 72 pulse beats (there aren't any such people, but let's assume it). Now, nicotine causes his pulse rate to increase to, let us say, 76 beats. The correct ratio between pulse and respiration is thus altered. The result is that the blood doesn't receive enough oxygen, since a certain amount is supposed to be absorbed into the blood with each pulse beat. The consequence of nicotine poisoning, therefore, is that the blood demands too much oxygen. The breathing process does not supply enough oxygen, and a slight shortness of breath occurs. This shortness of breath is, of course, so negligible that it escapes notice; after all, as I have told you, the human body can take a lot of abuse. Nevertheless, the use of nicotine always calls forth a definite, very slight shortness of breath. This slight shortness of breath causes with each breath a feeling of anxiety. Every shortness of breath causes a feeling of anxiety. It is easier to control a normal sensation of anxiety than this terribly slight anxiety, of which one is completely unconscious. When something like anxiety, fear or shock remains unnoticed it is a direct source of illness.

Such a source of illness is constantly present in a person who is a heavy smoker because, without realizing it, he is always filled with a certain anxiety. Now, you know that if you suffer from anxiety, your heart pumps more quickly. This leads you to realize that the heart of a person who constantly poisons himself with nicotine continuously beats somewhat too fast. When it beats too quickly, however, the heart thickens, just as the muscle of the upper arm, the biceps, grows thicker when it is constantly strained. Under some circumstances, this is not so bad, as long as the inner tissue doesn't tear. If the heart muscle—it is also a muscle—

becomes too thick from overexertion, however, it exerts pressure on all the other organs with the result, as a rule, that beginning from the heart the blood circulation becomes disturbed. The circulation of the blood cannot be initiated by the heart, but it can be disturbed when the heart is thickened.

The next consequence of a thickened heart is that the kidneys become ill, since it is due to the harmonious activities of heart and kidneys that the entire human bodily organization is kept functioning properly. The heart and kidneys must always work in harmony. Naturally, everything in the human being must harmonize, but the heart and kidneys are directly connected. It quickly becomes apparent that when something is amiss in the heart, the kidneys no longer function properly. Urinary elimination no longer works in the right way, with the result that the human being develops a much too rapid tempo of life and comes to wear himself out too quickly. A person who takes into his body too much nicotine in relation to his bodily proportions therefore will slowly but surely deteriorate. Actually, he gradually perishes from a variety of inner conditions of anxiety that influence the heart.

The effects of states of anxiety on the activities of the soul can easily be determined. In people who have introduced too much nicotine into their bodies, it becomes noticeable that gradually their power of thought is also impaired. The power of thought is impaired because the human being can no longer think properly when he lives in anxiety. Nicotine poisoning, therefore, can be recognized by the fact that such people's thoughts are no longer quite in order. They usually jump to conclusions much too quickly. They sometimes intensify this overly rapid judgement to paranoid thoughts. We can therefore say that the use of nicotine for pleasure actually undermines human health.

In all such matters, however, you must consider the other side. Smoking is something that has only come about in humanity's recent evolution. Originally, human beings did not smoke, and it is only recently that the use of tobacco has become fashionable. Now let us look at the other side of the coin.

Let us assume that a person's pulse beats only 68 instead of 72 times per minute. Such a person, whose blood circulation is not animated enough, now begins to smoke. You see, then his blood circulation is stimulated in the right direction, from 68 to 72, so that his blood circulation and breathing harmonize. If, therefore, a doctor notices that an illness is caused by weak blood circulation, he may even advise his patient to smoke.

As was said before, when the blood circulation is too rapid relative to breathing, one is dealing with terrible conditions of anxiety, which however do not become conscious. If for some reason a person's blood circulation is too weak, however, this makes itself felt by the fact that he goes around wanting to do something but not knowing what. This is also a characteristic phenomenon of illness; there are people who go around wanting something, but they do not know what it is that they want. Just think how many people go around without knowing what they want! One commonly says that they are dissatisfied with life. They are the people, who, for example, somehow drift into some profession, which then does not suit them, and so forth. This is really due to a blood circulation that is too weak. With such a person one can actually say that it is beneficial to administer nicotine to cure him. If smoking is agreeable to him, one need not prescribe nicotine in medicinal form, but one can advise him to smoke if previously he wasn't a smoker.

It is actually true that in recent times people who really do not know what they want have become more and more numerous. It is indeed easy in our modern age for people not to know what they want because, for the last three or four centuries, the majority of them have become unaccustomed to occupying themselves with anything spiritual. They go to their offices and busy themselves with something they actually dislike but that brings in money. They sit through their office hours, are even quite industrious, but they have no real interests except going to the theatre or reading newspapers. Gradually, things have been reduced to this. Even reading books, for example, has become a rarity today.

That this has all come about is due to the fact that people don't know at all what they want. They must be told what they want. Reading newspapers or going to the theatre stimulates the senses and the intellect but not the blood. When one must sit down and read some difficult book, the blood is stimulated. As soon as an effort has to be made to understand something, the blood is stimulated, but people do not want that any more. They quite dislike having to exert themselves to understand something. That is something quite repugnant to people. They do not want to understand anything! This unwillingness to understand causes their blood to thicken. Such thick blood circulates more slowly. As a result, a remedy is constantly required to bring this increasingly thick blood into motion. It is brought into motion when they stick a cigarette into their mouth. The blood doesn't become thinner, but the blood circulation becomes ever more difficult. This can cause people to become afflicted with various signs of old age at a time in life when this needn't yet occur.

This shows how extraordinarily delicate the human body's

activity is. Diagnostic results are obtained not only when the blood is examined but also when the manner in which a person behaves—whether he thinks slowly or quickly—is studied. You therefore can see, gentlemen, that if you wish to know something about the effect of nicotine, you must be thoroughly familiar with the entire circulatory and breathing processes.

Now, remember what I recently told you about how the blood is produced in the bone marrow. Essentially it comes from there. If the blood is produced in the bone marrow and the blood is made to circulate too quickly, then the bone marrow must also work faster than it should. As a result, the bones cannot keep up with their work, and then those creatures develop within the bones, those little creatures that devour us. Doctors such as Metchnikoff believed that these osteoclasts, as such little fellows are called, are the cause of human death. Metchnikoff said that if there were no osteoclasts, we would live forever. He held that they literally devour us. The fact is that the older we get, the more osteoclasts are present. It is true that our bones are gradually eaten by the osteoclasts, but seen from the opposite angle it is like fertilizing a field well—more will grow on it than if it were badly fertilized. For the human being, the introduction of nicotine into the body has a detrimental effect on the bones, but for these cannibalistic bone-devourers, the osteoclasts, it creates the best environment possible.

This is how it is in the world. A lazy thinker assumes that the world is fashioned by the Good Lord and so all must be well. Then one can ask why God allowed the osteoclasts to grow alongside the bones. If he had not allowed the osteoclasts to grow, we would not be slowly devoured throughout life. Instead, we could abuse our bones so terribly that something else would finally make them deteriorate. In any case, they could last for centuries if these little beasts were not contained within them.

It serves no purpose, however, to think lazily this way. The only useful thing is to examine the facts truly, to know that the delicate forces instrumental in building up the bones have their adversaries. These osteoclasts, too, are part of creation, and we have them within us by the millions. The older you get, the more of these osteoclasts you have. You have cannibals, though they are minute, always within you. Actual cannibals are not the most clever; the cleverest are those that we carry around within us in this way, and they find fertile ground when nicotine is introduced into the body.

You can recognize the extraordinary importance of thoroughly understanding the entire human being in order to determine how a given substance works in the human body.

12. Nutrition and Health

In this lecture Rudolf Steiner examines nutrition specifically from the perspective of health and healing and how a detailed knowledge of the spiritual as well as the materialistic constitution of the human being and of the substances in nature is necessary if proper remedies are to be found. What is poison in one context can heal a person in another. However, specifically with regard to diet, he also makes the subtle point that the positive or negative effect of the food we eat—if we move to a vegetarian diet, for example— depends as much on the harmony between our physical and spiritual organism as the actual food itself, that material change also needs to be accompanied by spiritual development. The human being must always be looked at in the round.

Today we will speak about something from the perspective of spiritual science which is of great value if it is understood in the proper way. We will look at a number of aspects regarding nutrition and methods of healing. But more so than in other areas, you must take into account that we can only pick out a few aphoristic details from an infinitely wide field and that it is very difficult to talk about it today in a language which will be generally understood. We can therefore only hint at it because in such extended circles we are not dealing with initiates who would be in a position to perceive the truth value in each word...

It is often said that the public are veritably mesmerized when the term 'poison' is used. It seems very obvious to say that poison should not enter the body! In this context people like to refer to 'naturopathy'. What should be understood by nature in the first place? And by poison? Nature also includes the effect which the poison of belladonna exercises on the human organism because it is a purely natural effect. Nature of course includes all effects that are governed by laws of nature. And what is poison? Water is a strong poison if a person were to drink it by the bucketful because then it has a very destructive effect. And arsenic is a very good thing if it is used in certain compounds. That is why a really detailed study of the human organism and the things outside in nature is required.

Paracelsus already had spoken in his intense language about how certain processes in the human body are connected with such in external nature, for example cholera and arsenic. That is also why he called a person stricken by cholera *arsenicus*, because he knew that the same factors are at work in cholera and arsenic and because he also recognized how these things harmonize. Here we have a process of nature which must first be understood.

Another thing which creates obstacles in seeking to come to an understanding with science is the materialistic way of thinking which has thrown a dubious light on all these questions. You may recall what we said about the effect of certain metals on the human organism. Now someone might well say that spiritual science is pure materialism if it says that the forces in the minerals and metals exercise material effects on the human organism. But spiritual science also knows that there is a certain relationship between matter and spirit. Anyone who represents a truly spiritual view of the world has recognized that such substances cannot be seen purely as matter but that soul and spirit lives in them like in a being enclosed by skin. In this sense the theosophist refers to the spirit which is incorporated in gold, in quartz, in arsenic or in the poison of belladonna. For the esotericist, the world is full of spiritual beings. The spirituality incorporated in lead has the relationship to the human organism which you heard about yesterday. For the theosophist, it is not a matter of seeking out all kinds of strange spiritual beings who have nothing to do with our world, but such ones that are contained in each piece of metal and everything else that surrounds us. In this way the spiritual view of the world spiritualizes matter. Spiritual analogies are based on real spiritual research.

This is not a matter of opposing specialist science. There must be specialization and one must not ignore external facts. But it is impossible to achieve an overall view of the world from a specialist knowledge. A doctor as an individual must know something about higher worlds. He will then organize his work quite differently from someone who does not know anything about the greater context. Then symptoms will also be assessed differently. An individual observation or experience might be seen as something quite minor when such a view arises from an overview of the whole. Like anyone working on culture must bring certain prerequisites with them, so the future will also demand that doctors are trained in spiritual science. We are talking here about something quite different from empirical abilities. Take Hahnemann, the founder of homoeopathy, as an example. There is a great difference between Paracelsus and Hahnemann. The sixteenth-century doctor was still clairvoyant to a certain extent. It was still a widespread characteristic. Hahnemann no longer was. He was only able to test the effect of the remedies through the experience of his senses.

There is an analogy for the relationship referred to here of the human being to the beings and objects of nature, namely, the relationship between the sexes which is primarily determined by attraction. It is a mysterious trait which attracts the sexes to one another, a force which works within what is alive. It should not be understood as something mystical in the negative sense of the word that a man feels attracted to a woman. Anyone who trains himself to be an esoteric observer of the world has a similar relationship to all living things around him, which we might call a universal one. Just as there is a specific relationship between one man and one woman, so there is a specific relationship between such a person and the phenomena of his environment. Anyone who has developed such forces in himself acquires the knowledge which allows him to recognize the relationship which a particular thing has to the human being. That also produces a knowledge of the effect of the healing forces.

Paracelsus did not first need to experiment just as the magnet does not need to experiment to attract the iron. He was able to say that the red foxglove has a certain healing power. Such knowledge will only return when the doctor understands that the intellect is not the only thing to matter but the inner attitude to life; when he knows that he himself must become quite a different person. When he has transformed the temperament, the character, the whole disposition of his soul, only then can he develop those powers of vision and knowledge with regard to the forces in the world which harmonize the human being. That will be possible in the not too distant future. The task of the spiritual-scientific understanding of the world is above all to state certain principles, some of which will follow these general considerations. Those who want to can gain a lot from them.

There are four things to consider here. The first is that there is a certain connection between what we call digestion and thinking. In other words, thinking is at a higher level what digestion is at a lower level. Both are intimately connected in the human organism as it lives on the physical plane. In concrete terms, it is part of thinking that one can draw logical conclusions, that one concept can be deduced from another. Such deductive activity in thinking is something very specific. One can do certain exercises to bring such thinking activity onto a certain track. What is achieved mentally in thinking activity when you undertake such logical exercises is achieved by a specific substance in the digestion, namely, coffee. That is not some fantastical assumption but a fact which can be verified. What you do to the stomach with coffee is the effect you achieve in the thinking when you undertake practical logical exercises. When you drink coffee, you promote logical consistency in the thinking in a certain way. And when people say that drinking coffee means an enhancement of the activity which is required to strengthen the thinking, that is accurate. But coffee only promotes logical thinking in a way which is involuntary; it works as if through compulsion. You feel a certain dependence within you, something like an effect from outside. If a person wishes to think logically but remain unfree he should drink a lot of coffee. But if he wants to think independently he must free himself precisely from those things which act on the lower parts; he must develop those forces in himself which come from the soul. But then he will also have the experience that after the corresponding exercise his stomach returns to normal or stays normal.

Another thing: ordered thinking is opposed by the kind of thinking which can never stick with a thought, unfocused thinking. It is scattered and is characterized by not being able to keep one thought with another. This thinking, too, has its correlation with the action of a particular substance on the digestion, and that is contained in tea. Tea indeed acts in the lower sphere like everything that causes the thoughts to wander in the upper sphere.

You can see that certain harmful effects of tea can under certain circumstances have a devastating effect. But don't think that a person who drinks tea for the whole of his life necessarily ends up being completely shredded inside. If he is not influenced in this way through tea, it shows that his organism possesses sufficient resistance . . .

If we return to the digestion and thinking once more, we will find that there is a lot to do in this field in particular. We should be clear that humanity must increasingly move over to a conscious way of feeding itself. Those who study in this field nevertheless often still make a certain mistake. This is that people want to learn too much about what they call 'nature'; they want to follow nothing but nature. Paracelsus said in this respect: one should not be a slave of nature. The doctor should go through nature's examination but he must be an artist, he must carry nature forward. And Paracelsus sees the real remedies not in what is taken directly from nature but in new products which are created from the spirit of nature. Thus Paracelsus anticipates an age in medicine which uses such new products as actual effective remedies. It is solely about a continuation of nature in this field.

If people today want to justify why a mixed diet is the right thing for human beings, they tend to argue that the ruminants are herbivores and have the appropriately developed stomach and the corresponding digestive tools. The carnivores are meat-eaters whose jaws and digestive tools are designed for eating meat. The teeth and digestive tools of the human being now are an intermediate thing between those of the ruminants and the carnivores. That is why nature itself indicates that human beings should eat a mixed diet. But everything in the world is in flux, in development and growth. The key thing is not how people look today but how they can change. If human beings move over to plant-based food, those organs will regress which are better for a meat diet and those organs will develop which are required for a plant-based diet. We have to take into consideration what things were like in the past and what might happen in the future. Hence we do not give people proper nourishment if we apply the current status but only if we take their development into consideration. Statistics and external facts will give you the external status, but they will not give you the direction in which the human being must move. We must to some extent also look at the world on a larger scale . . .

Now you will be able to see that one can, if necessary, intervene in this situation in a corrective way. A person can arrange his diet in such a way that he only needs a short time for digestion while another person might spend a long time doing so. Once again that gives us a deep insight into the human organism. Because if a person eats rice and is quickly finished with digesting it, then certain forces remain which he can then use for thinking. Another person who might eat wild duck and needs correspondingly longer for digestion may also be clever; but when he produces thoughts it is in reality his stomach which is thinking. The one person might be a weak thinker but thinking independently, the other a strong thinker but his thinking will not be independent. Once again we can draw a lesson from that.

To touch on something else still: the greatest care must be

taken to ensure that the body is not given too much or too
little protein. It is essential that the right measure is found.
Because in the digestion the proteins correspond to what
happens during the generation of ideas in the thinking. The
same activity which produces the productivity of the thinking
is produced through the proteins in the lower organism. If
human beings do not receive them in a balanced quantity,
they create a surplus of such forces which in the activity of the
abdomen reflect what creates the ideas in the upper organism. But human beings are meant increasingly to become the
masters of their ideas. Hence the intake of protein should
remain within certain limits, otherwise they will be over-
whelmed by the ideas that arise in a way of which they should
become independent. That was what Pythagoras meant
when he told his pupils that they should abstain from beans!

Of course people come and point out that a particular
person who eats rice is still a weak thinker. But the point is
that such a person has not developed in other respects. It is
not enough to know the rules and think that all that is
required is to follow them. If the lower and upper organism
are not in harmony you can also cause damage in this way.
Take someone who has turned vegetarian. The activities in
the lower organism take place in a very specific way in this
new vegetarian. Certain forces are no longer material but
become spiritual. But if they are not used, they have a detrimental effect and can even compromise the activity of the
brain. Someone who works as nothing but a banker or an
ordinary academic can do himself a great deal of damage if he
does not assimilate spiritual ideas through the forces which
are saved through his vegetarian lifestyle. Hence a vegetarian
must also begin to lead a spiritual life, otherwise he would do
better to remain a meat-eater; his memory might begin to

suffer, certain parts of the brain could be damaged, and so on. It is not sufficient merely to eat fruit and expect that as a result the highest spheres of spiritual life will thereby become accessible.

Sources

1. Nutrition in the Light of Spiritual Science
'Problems of nutrition', Munich, 8 January 1909, tr. Maria St Goar, in *Problems of Nutrition* (GA 68) (New York: Anthroposophic Press, 1969)

'Ernährungsfragen im Lichte der Geisteswissenschaft', Berlin, 17 December 1908, extract tr. for this volume by Christian von Arnim, in *Wo und wie findet man den Geist?* (GA 57) (Dornach: Rudolf Steiner Verlag, 1984)

2. The Penetration of Substance with Spirit
'The penetration of substance with spirit', Dornach, 10 November 1923, tr. revised by Matthew Barton, in *Harmony of the Creative Word* (GA 230) (London: Rudolf Steiner Press, 2001)

3. Nutrition from a Cosmic Perspective
'The question of food', The Hague, 21 March 1913, tr. revised by Jann Gates, in *The Effects of Esoteric Development* (GA 145) (Great Barrington, MA: SteinerBooks, 2007)

4. Nutrition and the Human Body
'Nutrition', Dornach, 23 January 1923, tr. A.R. Meuss, in *From Elephants to Einstein* (GA 352) (London: Rudolf Steiner Press, 1998)

5. Healthy Nutrition and the Quality of Food
'Questions of nutrition—children's nutrition—hardening of the arteries—manuring', Dornach, 2 August 1924, tr. revised by Matthew Barton, in *From Sunspots to Strawberries* (GA 354) (London: Rudolf Steiner Press, 2002)

6. The Processes of Digestion

'The process of digestion in physical as well as soul-spiritual terms', Dornach, 16 September 1922, tr. revised by Matthew Barton, in *From Crystals to Crocodiles* (GA 347) (London: Rudolf Steiner Press, 2002)

7. The Effect of Plant, Raw Food, Vegetarian and Meat Diets

'On the relationship between foods and the human being—raw food and vegetarian diets', Dornach, 31 July 1924, tr. revised by Matthew Barton, in *From Sunspots to Strawberries* (GA 354) (London: Rudolf Steiner Press, 2002)

8. Potatoes, Beetroots and Radishes and the Spiritual in Human Beings

'Ernährungsfragen. Wirkung von Kartoffeln, Rübe und Rettich', Dornach, 18 July 1923, extracts tr. for this volume by Christian von Arnim, in *Rhytmen im Kosmos und im Menschenwesen* (GA 350) (Dornach: Rudolf Steiner Verlag, 1962)

9. The Effects of Protein, Fats, Carbohydrates and Salts

'Die Wirkung von Eiweiß, Fetten, Kohlehydraten und Salzen', Dornach, 22 September 1923, extracts tr. for this volume by Christian von Arnim, in *Rhytmen im Kosmos und im Menschenwesen* (GA 350) (Dornach: Rudolf Steiner Verlag, 1962)

10. The Effects of Alcohol

'The effects of alcohol', Dornach, 8 January 1923, tr. revised by Matthew Barton, in *From Comets to Cocaine* (GA 348) (London: Rudolf Steiner Press, 2000)

11. The Effects of Nicotine

'The effect of nicotine. Vegetarian and meat diets. On taking absinthe. Twin births', Dornach, 13 January 1923, tr. revised by

Matthew Barton, in *From Comets to Cocaine* (GA 348) (London: Rudolf Steiner Press, 2000)

12. Nutrition and Health

'Ernährungsfragen und Heilmethoden', Berlin, 22 October 1906, extracts tr. for this volume by Christian von Arnim, in *Ursprung-simpulse der Geisteswissenschaft* (GA 96) (Dornach: Rudolf Steiner Verlag, 1989)

Note on Rudolf Steiner's Lectures

The lectures and addresses contained in this volume have been translated from the German, which is based on stenographic and other recorded texts that were in most cases never seen or revised by the lecturer. Hence, due to human errors in hearing and transcription, they may contain mistakes and faulty passages. Every effort has been made to ensure that this is not the case. Some of the lectures were given to audiences more familiar with anthroposophy; these are the so-called 'private' or 'members' lectures. Other lectures, like the written works, were intended for the general public. The difference between these, as Rudolf Steiner indicates in his *Autobiography*, is twofold. On the one hand, the members' lectures take for granted a background in and commitment to anthroposophy; in the public lectures this was not the case. At the same time, the members' lectures address the concerns and dilemmas of the members, while the public work arises from and directly addresses Steiner's own understanding of universal needs. Nevertheless, as Rudolf Steiner stresses: 'Nothing was ever said that was not solely the result of my direct experience of the growing content of anthroposophy. There was never any question of concessions to the prejudices and preferences of the members. Whoever reads these privately printed lectures can take them to represent anthroposophy in the fullest sense. Thus it was possible without hesitation—when the complaints in this direction became too persistent—to depart from the custom of circulating this material "For members only". But it must be borne in mind that faulty passages do occur in these reports not revised by myself.' Earlier in the same chapter, he states: 'Had I been able to correct them [*the private lectures*], the restriction *for members only* would have been unnecessary from the beginning.' The original German editions on which this text is based were published by Rudolf Steiner Verlag, Dornach, Switzerland in the collected edition (*Gesamtausgabe*, 'GA') of Rudolf Steiner's work. All publications are edited by the Rudolf Steiner Nachlassverwaltung (estate), which wholly owns both Rudolf Steiner Verlag and the Rudolf Steiner Archive.